Aiming for a sky-high score in Physics?

You've come to the right place — this CGP Exam Practice Workbook
is the perfect launchpad for sending your grade into orbit!

It's packed with challenging Grade 8-9 exam-style questions, sorted by topic and
perfectly matched to the Edexcel International GCSE Physics course*. What's more,
there are two sections of mixed practice to test you on a wider range of skills.

We've even included step-by-step answers at the back, so it's easy to check
your work and find out how to pick up any marks you missed out on.

* It covers all the toughest Physics topics from Edexcel's International GCSE Science Double Award too.

CGP — still the best! ☺

Our sole aim here at CGP is to produce the highest quality books —
carefully written, immaculately presented and dangerously close to being funny.

Then we work our socks off to get them out to you
— at the cheapest possible prices.

Published by CGP

Editors:
Caroline Purvis, Stephen Walters, Sarah Williams

Contributors:
James Allen, Stuart Burditt, Ian Connor

With thanks to Mark Edwards, Glenn Rogers and Karen Wells for the proofreading.

With thanks to Ana Pungartnik for the copyright research.

Data used to construct stopping distance graphs on page 47 from the Highway Code.
Contains public sector information licensed under the Open Government Licence v3.0.
http://www.nationalarchives.gov.uk/doc/open-government-licence/version/3/

ISBN: 978 1 78908 238 8

Clipart from Corel®

Illustrations by: Sandy Gardner Artist, email sandy@sandygardner.co.uk
Printed by Elanders Ltd, Newcastle upon Tyne.

Based on the classic CGP style created by Richard Parsons.

Contents

✓ Use the tick boxes to check off the topics you've completed.

Paper 2

The questions in this book test both Physics Paper 1 and Physics Paper 2 material. Some material is needed for Paper 2 only — we've marked Paper 2 questions in Sections 1-8 with brackets like this one.

If you're doing a Science (Double Award) qualification you don't need to learn the Paper 2 material.

Exam Tips

Exam Basics

1) For the Edexcel International GCSE in Physics, you'll sit <u>two exam papers</u> at the <u>end</u> of your course.

Paper	Time	No. of marks
1	2 hours	110
2	1 hr 15 mins	70

2) If you're doing the Edexcel International GCSE Science Double Award, you won't sit Paper 2.

3) Some material in the specification will only be tested in <u>Paper 2</u>. In Sections 1-8 of this book, the questions that cover Paper 2 material are marked with a <u>Paper 2 bracket</u>.

You Need to Understand the Command Words

<u>Command words</u> are the words in a question that tell you <u>what to do</u>.
If you don't know what they mean, you might not be able to answer the questions properly.

Describe — This means you need to recall <u>facts</u> or write about what something is <u>like</u>.

Explain — You have to <u>give reasons</u> for something or say <u>why</u> or <u>how</u> something happens.

Suggest — You need to use your knowledge to <u>work out</u> the answer. It'll often be something you haven't been taught, but you should be able to use what you know to figure it out.

Calculate — This means you'll have to use <u>numbers</u> from the question to <u>work something out</u>. You'll probably have to get your calculator out.

Here are a Few Handy Hints

1) **Always, always, always make sure you <u>read the question properly</u>.**
   This is a simple tip but it's really important. When you've got so much knowledge swimming round in your head it can be tempting to jump right in and start scribbling your answer down. But take time to make <u>absolutely sure</u> you're answering the question you've been asked.

2) **Take your <u>time</u> with <u>unfamiliar contexts</u>.**
   Examiners like to test you really understand what you've learnt by asking you to apply your knowledge in <u>different ways</u>. Some of these contexts can be quite tricky but don't let them trip you up — read all the information you're given <u>really carefully</u> and, if you don't understand it, <u>read it again</u>. You can make notes alongside the question or underline certain bits if it helps you to focus on the <u>important</u> information.

3) **Look at the <u>number of marks</u> a question is worth.**
   The number of marks gives you a pretty good clue as to <u>how much</u> to write. So if a question is worth four marks, make sure you write four decent points. And there's no point writing an essay for a question that's only worth one mark — it's just a waste of your time.

4) **Show <u>each step</u> in your <u>calculations</u>.**
   You might be a bit of a whizz at maths and be confident that your final answer to a question will be right, but everyone makes mistakes — especially when under the pressure of an exam. Always write things out in <u>steps</u> then, even if your final answer's wrong, you'll probably pick up <u>some marks</u> for your method.

5) **Pay attention to the <u>time</u>.**
   After all those hours of revision it would be a shame to miss out on marks because you didn't have <u>time</u> to even attempt some of the questions. If you find that you're really struggling with a question, just <u>leave it</u> and <u>move on</u> to the next one. You can always <u>go back to it</u> at the end if you've got enough time.

   These handy hints might help you pick up as many marks as you can in the exams — but they're no use if you haven't learnt the stuff in the first place. So make sure you revise well and do as many practice questions as you can.

Forces and Moments

1 A rocket is launched on a mission to land on the Moon.

The diagram below shows the rocket at a particular point in time as it
moves directly upwards through the Earth's atmosphere.
The upwards force acting on the rocket from the engines is 40.0×10^6 N.
The rocket has a weight of 7.60×10^6 N.
The air resistance acting on the rocket is 9.40×10^6 N.

a) Draw **one** vector arrow from the × marked on the diagram to represent the magnitude and
direction of the resultant force acting on the rocket. Use a scale of 1 mm = 10^6 N.

$$40 \times 10^6 - 9.40 \times 10^6$$
$$= 30.60 \times 10^6$$

[2]

The Earth's gravitational field strength, g, varies with the distance from the Earth,
and can be calculated using the equation:

$$g = \frac{GM_E}{r^2}$$

where: r = the distance from the centre of the Earth in m
M_E = the mass of the Earth in kg = 5.97×10^{24} kg
G = gravitational constant = 6.67×10^{-11} N m²/kg²
The distance of the Moon from the centre of the Earth is 3.84×10^8 m.

b) The weight of the Moon due to the Earth's gravitational field is 1.98×10^{20} N.
Calculate the mass of the Moon.

$$g = \frac{GM}{r} \quad \rightarrow \quad gr^2 = Gm$$

$$\frac{gr^2}{G} \qquad m = \frac{gr^2}{G} = \frac{(1.98 \times 10^{20}) \times (3.84 \times 10^8)^2}{6.67 \times 10^{-11}}$$

$$g = \frac{6.67 \times 10^{-11} \times 5.97 \times 10^{24}}{(3.84 \times 10^1)^2}$$

$$= 2.7004 \times 10^{-3}$$

$$w = m \times g \quad \rightarrow \quad m = \frac{w}{g} = \frac{1.98 \times 10^{20}}{2.7004 \times 10^3}$$

$$= 7.332 \times 10^{22}$$

Mass = ...7.33×10²²...... kg

[5]

[Total 7 marks]

2   A plank is in equilibrium and rests on two supports.

The plank is 6.0 m long, has a uniform density and a mass of 9.4 kg.
A mass of 8.8 kg is placed on the plank at point B, as shown in the diagram below.

There is a support at point A, at one end of the plank. Another support is positioned at point C.
The distance from A to C is twice the distance from C to the end of the plank, D.
Point B is halfway between the supports.

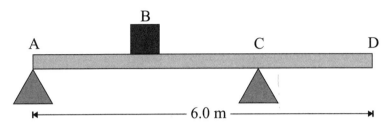

a) Calculate the upwards force acting on the plank at point A.
   Gravitational field strength, $g = 10$ N/kg.

the weight $w = mg = 9.4 kg \times 10 N/kg = 94 N$

$8.8 \times 10 = 88 kg$ clockwise = anticlock wise

AC = 4m
CD = 2m
AB = 2m

$F_A \times 4 = (88 \times 2) + (94 \times 1)$

$F_A = 67.5 N$

$\approx 68 N$

Force = ...6.8...... N

[5]

Levers can be used to vary the force needed to lift a load.
The mass at point B can be raised in three different ways:

•   by pressing down at point D and pivoting about C, or,

•   by lifting up at D and pivoting about A, or,

•   by lifting up at A and pivoting about C.

b) Which of these methods requires the largest force to raise the mass by the same height?

☒ A   Pressing down on the plank at point D.

☐ B   Lifting up the plank at point D.

☐ C   Lifting up the plank at point A.

☐ D   It requires the same force to move the block by all three methods.

[1]

[Total 6 marks]

Exam Practice Tip

Some questions will involve a lot of variables and additional information. As you work through
the question, it may be helpful to add labels and notes to the diagrams you've been given.
This can help you keep track of extra information and calculations all in one place.

Score:

13

Motion

1 An average speed camera calculates the average speed of a car by measuring the time it takes to travel between two sensors that are a set distance apart.

A car is travelling down a road, and passes the first sensor of an average speed camera. Just after the car passes the first sensor, the car travels a distance of 740 m in 27 s. It then travels 1400 m in 50 s, and finally travels another 360 m before passing the second sensor. The average speed camera calculates the car's average speed between the sensors as 27.2 m/s.

a) Calculate the time it took for the car to travel the last 360 m.

$$26.1925 \qquad V = \frac{d}{t} \rightarrow t = \frac{d}{V} = \frac{360}{26.1925}$$

$$740 + 1400 + 360 = 2500m = 13.74\cancel{4}$$

$$t = \frac{2500}{27.2} = 91.911 \qquad \approx 14s$$

$$91.911 - 27 - 50 = 14.911 = 14.9$$

$$\frac{740}{27} = 27.\dot{4}0\dot{7}$$

$$\frac{1400}{50} = 28$$

Time = ...**14.9**........ s

[3]

The distance-time graph below shows the first 300 s of the car's journey, before it reached the speed camera.

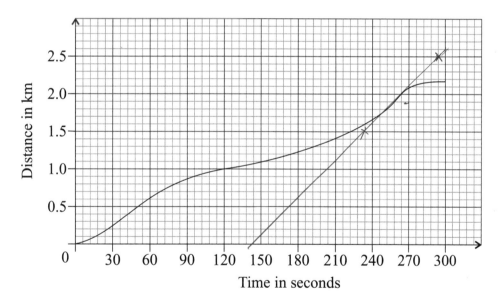

b) Calculate the maximum speed reached by the car during the first 300 s of the journey. Give your answer in km/h and to two significant figures.

$$\frac{2.5 - 1.5}{294 - 234} = 0.016 \ m/s$$

$$= 62.4 \approx 62 \ km/h$$

Speed = ...**62**........ km/h

[5]

[Total 8 marks]

Section 1 — Forces and Motion

2   A ferry is carrying passengers between two islands.

The velocity-time graph of the ferry during its journey is shown below.

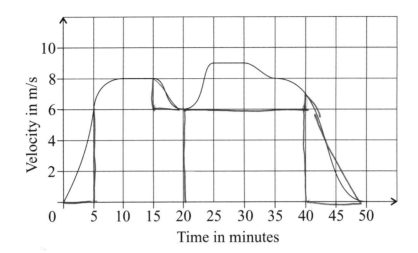

a) The speed of boats is often measured in knots. 1 knot ~ 0.5 m/s.
    Which of the following is the maximum speed reached by the ferry during its journey?

    ☐   **A**   4.5 knots
    ☐   **B**   15.5 knots
    ☒   **C**   18.0 knots
    ☐   **D**   4.0 knots

[1]

b) Estimate the average speed of the ferry during its journey.

$2 \times 5 \times 60 = 600$ m $31 \times 600 = 18600$ m

31 squares

3000 s $18600 \div 3000$

Average speed = ...6.2.................... m/s
[4]
[Total 5 marks]

Exam Practice Tip

Remember to pay close attention to the labels on graphs. You may be familiar with the quantities
the graph is showing, but the units used and the scales of the axes can be more unusual. Make
sure you take this into account when reading from the graph and making any calculations from it.

Score:

13

Section 1 — Forces and Motion

More on Motion

1 A child is throwing stones directly down into a pond from a height of 0.75 m above the surface. It can be assumed that air resistance is negligible and the stone accelerates downwards at 10 m/s².

a) A stone is thrown with an initial speed of 0.9 m/s.
Calculate the time taken for the stone to hit the surface of the water after being thrown.

$$V^2 = U^2 + (2 \times a \times s)$$

Time = ... s

[5]

The velocity-time graph of the stone from the point at which it is thrown is shown below. The dotted line shows the point at which the stone enters the water.

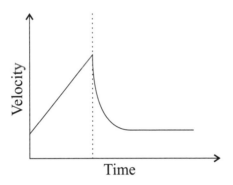

b) Using the graph, describe the forces acting on the stone as it falls through the air and water. Your answer should include a description of how the forces affect the stone's motion.

....

....

....

....

....

....

....

....

....

....

[5]

[Total 10 marks]

2   A student is investigating how the force applied to a trolley affects its acceleration. They use the set-up shown below. The student changes the force on the trolley by altering the angle of the ramp.

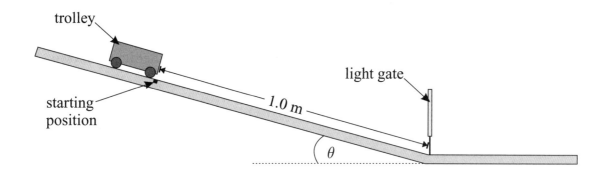

The trolley is held at rest at the starting position. It is released and allowed to roll down the ramp.

The light gate measures the final velocity of the trolley at the bottom of the ramp.
The student uses this to calculate the acceleration down the ramp.
The student also calculates the resultant force acting on the trolley in the direction of its motion.

The graph of their results is shown below.

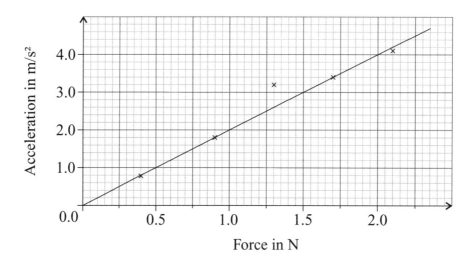

a)   Determine the mass of the trolley.

Mass = ... kg

[3]

When the resultant force was 1.3 N, the student recorded an anomalous result for acceleration. This was because the trolley had a non-zero initial velocity.
At a force of 1.3 N, the light gate recorded a final velocity of 2.53 m/s.

b) Calculate the initial velocity of the trolley for the anomalous result.
Give your answer to two significant figures.

Initial velocity = ... m/s
[5]

This experiment can be used to model the behaviour of a full-size car as it rolls down a hill. Assuming friction is negligible and the only force acting to move a car down a hill is its weight, a car will accelerate down a hill with an incline of 10° at approximately 1.7 m/s².

c) Estimate the size of the braking force which must be applied in order for a car to remain at a constant speed as it rolls down a hill with a 10° incline.

Force = ... N
[3]
[Total 11 marks]

3 A parachutist falling towards the Earth exerts an attractive force of 680 N on the Earth. Explain the cause of this force and explain why the Earth does not noticeably move towards the person.

....
....
....
....
....
....
....
....
....
[Total 4 marks]

Paper 2

Exam Practice Tip
It can be easy to feel like you've missed something and panic if a question doesn't seem to supply you with all the data needed, but if the command word is 'estimate' you can generally relax. The examiners are testing that you can come up with a realistic value for missing data to complete the calculation.

Score: ____
25

Section 1 — Forces and Motion

Stopping Distances and Momentum

1 Two people are investigating each other's reaction times.

Person 1 measures the reaction time of person 2 by dropping a ruler between their thumb and index finger. Person 2 has to catch the ruler as soon as possible after noticing that it is falling.

Person 2's arm is resting on the table with their hand free to catch the ruler. The 0.0 cm mark on the ruler is initially held level with person 2's thumb.

a) i) Person 1 measures person 2's reaction time to be 0.21 s.
Calculate the distance the ruler fell before person 2 caught it.
Give your answer in centimetres. Acceleration due to gravity = 10 m/s^2.

Distance = ... cm

[5]

ii) Suggest **two** changes that could be made to this experiment to improve the accuracy of the measurements. Explain your answers.

1. ....

....

....

2. ....

....

....

[4]

b) Person 3 has a reaction time of 0.18 s and person 4 has a reaction time of 0.23 s. Predict whether person 3 or person 4 would be able to stop a car they were driving in a shorter distance. Assume all conditions relating to the car and the road are identical. Explain your answer.

....

....

....

....

[3]

[Total 12 marks]

2　An engineer is testing a rifle. When the rifle is fired, the rifle 'jumps' backwards at the same time as firing the bullet. This is known as recoil.

a)　Explain why it is not possible to fire the rifle without the rifle recoiling.

....

....

....

[2]

b)　Suggest **one** change that could be made to a rifle to reduce its recoil velocity.
Explain your answer.

....

....

....

[2]

c)　A bullet with a mass of 10.0 g is fired to the right from a rifle with a mass of 4.00 kg.
The rifle recoils with a velocity of 1.00 m/s to the left.
The bullet strikes a stationary wooden block with a mass of 500 g and becomes lodged in it.
Calculate the velocity of the wooden block directly after the bullet becomes lodged in it.
Assume the speed of the bullet remains constant as it travels from the rifle to the block.
Give your answer to three significant figures.

Velocity = ... m/s
[5]

d)　When a person fires a rifle, they often hold the back of the rifle against their shoulder.
Rifles can be fitted with deformable pads on the back as a safety feature.
Explain how the deformable pads act as a safety feature.

....

....

....

....

....

[3]

[Total 12 marks]

Section 1 — Forces and Motion

3   A 1450 kg car is travelling at 22.4 m/s along a dry road. After noticing a hazard, the driver applies the brakes, causing the car to decelerate until it comes to rest.

a) The average braking force acting on the car is 9570 N.
Calculate the car's braking distance.

Braking distance = ... m

[5]

b) The driver's thinking distance is 14.6 m.
Calculate the total time between the driver first noticing the hazard and the car coming to a stop.

Time = ... s

[5]

c) A student makes the following hypothesis:
Assuming the force slowing the car down and all other conditions were the same,
it would take four times as much time for it to stop after the driver applied the brakes
if its initial speed was doubled.
Explain whether the student's hypothesis is correct.

....

....

....

....

[2]

[Total 12 marks]

Exam Practice Tip

You won't always be told if you need to use a value you calculated in an earlier question part to work out an answer, so make sure you keep your eyes peeled if you're asked to do more than one calculation in a row — you don't want to end up calculating the same thing twice!

Score: ☐

36

Circuits

1   A student has connected a circuit, shown below. The circuit contains a
    6.0 V cell, a thermistor, a 1.0 kΩ resistor and two voltmeters, V_1 and V_2.

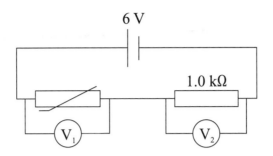

a)   The current through the thermistor is 0.50 A. The voltmeter V_1 reads 5.5 V.
     The current consists of a flow of electrons and each electron carries a charge of 1.6×10^{-19} C.
     Calculate the number of electrons that will flow through the thermistor in 2.0 hours.

Number of electrons = ...
[3]

b)   The circuit is moved to a different room, where the temperature is 16 °C.
     The reading on V_1 is now 0.25 V.
     Calculate the resistance of the thermistor when the external temperature is 16 °C.

Resistance = ... Ω
[5]

c)   An LED is added to the circuit, connected in series with the other components.
     State and explain the effect that this has on the current in the circuit.

....

....

....

....
[3]
[Total 11 marks]

2   A student conducts an experiment to find how the length of a wire affects its resistance. The graph of her results is shown below.

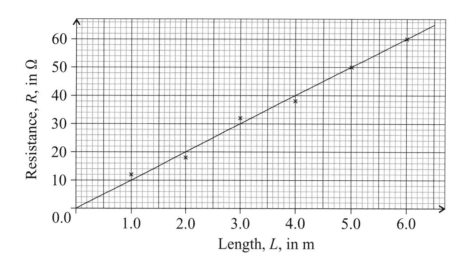

a) i) Determine the equation of the graph's line of best fit, in terms of resistance, R, and length, L.

Equation: ....

[2]

ii) A 0.375 m length of this wire is used in a circuit.
A potential difference of 500 mV is applied across the wire.
Calculate the current that flows through the wire. Give your answer to three significant figures.

Current = ... A

[5]

b) The resistance, R, of a given length of wire is related to its cross-sectional area, A, by the equation:

$$R = \frac{k}{A}$$

where k is a constant for wires of the material used.
The wire the student used in her experiment has a cross-sectional area of 0.11 mm².
A second wire made from the same material has a cross-sectional area of 0.44 mm².
Calculate the resistance of a 1.2 m length of this second wire.

[5]

[Total 12 marks]

Section 2 — Electricity

3   A student creates a circuit containing a variable power supply,
a 1.6 Ω resistor and component X connected in series.

A current-voltage graph for component X is shown below.

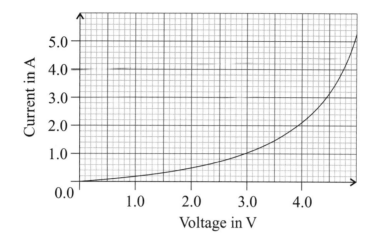

a) Using the graph, explain how the total resistance of the circuit changes as the voltage of the power
supply is increased.

....

....

....

....

....

....

[3]

b) The voltage across component X is 3.8 V.
Calculate the amount of time it will take for component X to transfer 1.0 kJ of energy.

Time = ... s

[4]

c) The voltage across component X is increased. Describe the effect, if any, that this will have on
the amount of energy transferred per second by the component as current flows through it.

....

....

[1]

[Total 8 marks]

Section 2 — Electricity

4 A rollercoaster uses an electric motor to push each car round an uneven section of track.

A joulemeter is connected to a data logger and used to monitor the energy transferred by the motor. The graph produced by the data logger is shown below.

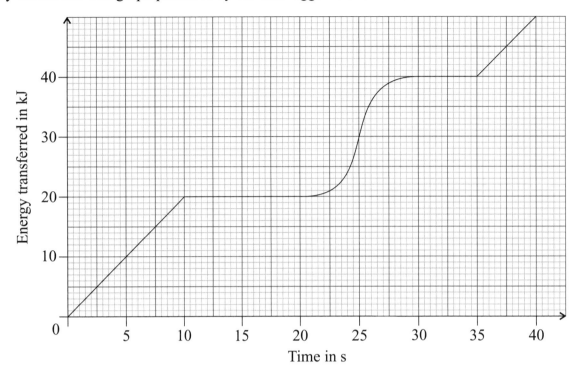

a) Between 20 s and 30 s, a total of 12 C of charge passes through the motor.
Using the graph, calculate the average potential difference across the motor during this time.
Give your answer to two significant figures.

Average potential difference = ... V

[5]

b) The average current through the supply cable that connects the motor to the electricity supply is 12 A. The resistance of the cable is 250 mΩ.
Calculate the average power wasted due to heating in the supply cable.

Average power = ... A

[4]

[Total 9 marks]

Exam Practice Tip

If you're given a graph, diagram or table and told to use it, you'll need to explicitly refer to it in your answer. That's easy enough if you're asked to do a calculation, but when writing an explanation make sure you stay focussed on the information and don't start talking about the topic too generally.

Score: ⬜

40

Section 2 — Electricity

Electrostatic Charges and Their Uses

1 An electrostatic paint sprayer is often used to paint car bodies and bicycle frames.

a) i) Some electrons are removed from the paint droplets as they leave the nozzle of the sprayer. Explain how this creates a fine mist of paint.

....

....

....

[2]

ii) Each paint droplet has a charge of 1.9×10^{-12} C.
In one minute, 4.2×10^{10} droplets pass out of the nozzle.
Calculate the size of the current flowing out of the nozzle.

Current = ... A

[4]

b) The object being painted is often given an opposite charge to the paint. Explain how this would help to produce an even coat of paint.

....

....

....

....

[3]

c) Explain why the operator of the paint sprayer must be earthed for their safety while using the paint sprayer.

....

....

....

[2]

[Total 11 marks]

2 A photocopier uses a charged image plate to create copies of documents.

a) Explain how the photocopier uses electrostatic charges to produce a copy of a page.

....

....

....

....

....

....

....

....

[4]

b) The photocopier is connected to the 230 V mains. To photocopy one sheet of paper, it must transfer 1.47×10^3 J of energy. Calculate the amount of charge that flows through the photocopier if 550 sheets of paper are copied.

Charge C

[4]

c) An office worker walks across a carpet to the photocopier. The soles of the worker's shoes and the carpet are both made of insulating materials. When the worker touches the photocopier, they experience a shock. Explain in terms of the movement of electrons what causes the worker to experience a shock.

....

....

....

....

....

[3]

[Total 11 marks]

Exam Practice Tip

Make sure you pay attention to the number of marks given for explanation questions — it'll help you work out what level of detail the examiners expect you to go into. There's no point spending valuable time showing everything you know about a topic when they're only after a couple of points.

Score:

22

Properties of Waves

1   A student sets up a ripple tank in a dark room.

She puts a screen beneath the tank, then sets up a lamp above the tank. She attaches a signal generator to the dipper in the tank. When she turns the signal generator on, ripples are generated and their shadows can be seen on the screen below. The shadow lines are the same size as the waves. Her experimental set-up is shown below.

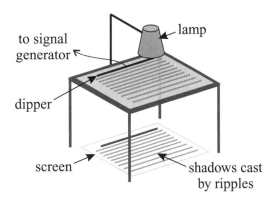

a)   The student finds that the total distance between the first and last of ten shadow lines is 27 cm.
The waves have a period of 0.25 s.
Calculate the speed of the waves produced by the dipper.

Speed = ... m/s
[5]

b)   The student replaces the lamp with a stroboscope but keeps the rest of the set-up the same.
A stroboscope flashes a bright light at regular time intervals.
The student adjusts the time interval of the flashes until the ripples appear to stop moving.
Give the shortest possible time interval that could be used by the student to achieve this effect.
Explain your answer.

....

....

....
[2]

[Total 7 marks]

Exam Practice Tip

Practicals — there's no escaping them, even when you're in the exam hall. If you find yourself face to face with questions about an unfamiliar experiment, keep calm and bust out those planning and data handling skills you nurtured during those many happy hours spent in the school lab.

Score: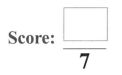

7

Wave Behaviour

1   A high-speed train sounds its horn as it passes a platform.

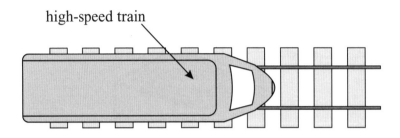

high-speed train

a) Describe how the frequency of the sound heard by observers on the
    platform changes as the train moves towards and then away from the platform.
    Explain why this variation occurs.

    ....

    ....

    ....

    ....

    ....

    [4]

b) The horn generates sound by vibrating a thin sheet of metal. Explain how the characteristics of
    the sheet's motion relate to the pitch and loudness of the sound waves it produces.

    ....

    ....

    ....

    ....

    [2]

c) An electromagnetic sensor is fitted to the train to detect anyone illegally
    breaking into the train at night. Suggest and explain **one** type of
    electromagnetic radiation that could be used for this application.

    ....

    ....

    ....

    ....

    [2]

    [Total 8 marks]

2   A ray of light enters a transparent block and is internally reflected, as shown.

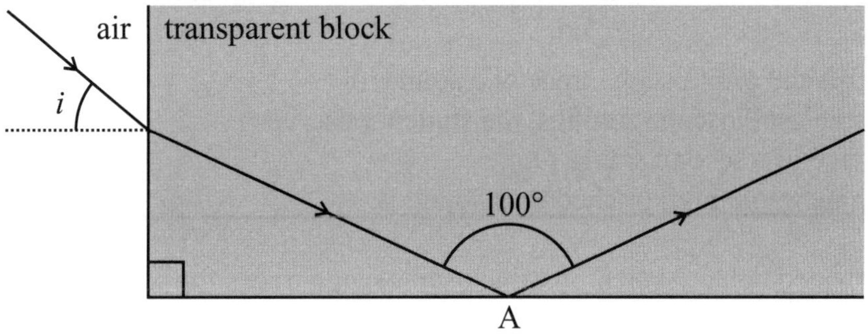

Diagram **not** drawn accurately.

a) As the light enters the transparent block its wave speed is reduced but its frequency is unchanged. Explain how the light's wavelength is affected. Justify your answer.

....

....

....

....

[2]

The angle of incidence, labelled i, is the angle the incoming ray of light makes with the normal to the block's surface. If i is increased by any amount the ray of light will no longer undergo total internal reflection at the point labelled A but will instead be refracted across this boundary.

b) Calculate the refractive index, n, of the transparent block.

$n =$ ....
[4]

c) Calculate i, the angle of incidence of the incoming ray of light.

$\theta =$ ....$^{\circ}$
[5]
[Total 11 marks]

Section 3 — Waves

3 A student produces sound using a signal generator connected to a speaker.
They then measure this sound using a microphone connected to an oscilloscope.

The student observes the oscilloscope trace of a sound, A.
Then, using the same oscilloscope settings, the student observes
the oscilloscope trace of a second sound, B.
Sound A is louder and more high pitched than sound B.

a) Using the axes provided below, sketch possible oscilloscope traces for sounds A and B.

sound A

sound B

[2]

b) The signal generator can be used to adjust the period of the sound wave emitted by the speakers.
Starting with a period of 0.004 s, the student repeatedly doubles the period of the sound wave
until it is no longer audible to the human ear.
Suggest approximately how many times the student doubles the sound wave's period.
You should justify your answer with a calculation.

.... times

[3]

[Total 5 marks]

Exam Practice Tip

If, like me, the word 'sketch' sends your mind back to unsuccessful art classes — don't panic. The examiner isn't looking for a masterpiece, just a clear drawing that demonstrates you understand the physics. If you're still worried, you can include labels that really help you get your point across.

Score:

24

Energy Transfers

1 A stone is thrown horizontally into a box that is hanging from the ceiling. The stone is caught in the box and the box swings upwards, as shown in the diagram below.

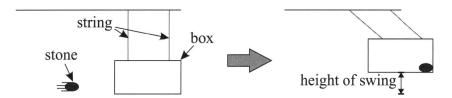

After the stone lands in the box, the swing reaches a maximum height of 20 cm.
The stone has a mass of 20 g and the box has a mass of 100 g.
The gravitational field strength is 10 N/kg.

a) Calculate the speed of the stone just before it hit the box. You may assume that all the energy in the kinetic energy store of the stone was transferred to the gravitational potential energy stores of the stone and the box.

Speed = ... m/s

[5]

The box begins to swing back and forth with the stone inside. The graph below shows how the total energy in the gravitational potential energy stores of the box and the stone changes over time.

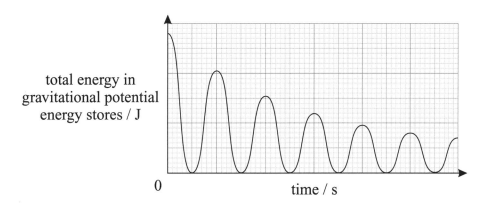

b) Explain why the peaks shown on the graph become smaller over time.

....

....

....

....

[1]

[Total 6 marks]

2   A 140 g snooker ball is at rest on a smooth, flat table.

a) A player strikes the ball with their cue.
The ball moves 2.3 mm while it is in contact with the cue, before moving away at a speed of 1.6 m/s.
Calculate the average resultant force on the snooker ball while it is in contact with the cue.

Force = ... N

[5]

b) The snooker player leaves a white ball and a black ball outside on a sunny day. Both balls
are made of the same material and are initially at a temperature of 20 ºC. After 2 hours, the
temperature of the black ball is 27 ºC and the temperature of the white ball is 22 ºC.
Suggest an explanation for this difference in temperature.

....

....

....

[2]

[Total 7 marks]

3   A student is carrying out an experiment to investigate thermal energy transfer
in lead. She heats a 6.0 kg block of lead using the apparatus shown.

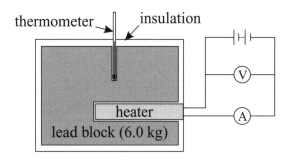

a) The circuit supplies 0.10 kW of useful power to the lead.
The student calculates that, during 9.0 minutes of use, the circuit wastes 300 J of energy
to the thermal energy stores of the surroundings.
Calculate the efficiency of the circuit.

Efficiency = ... %

[5]

Section 4 — Energy Resources and Energy Transfer

The student plots the results of her experiment on a graph to show how the temperature of the lead changes with time.

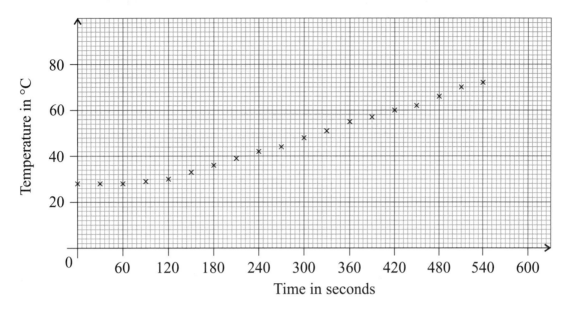

b) i) Estimate what the temperature of the lead would be 10 minutes after the start of the experiment if she continued heating the lead block.

Temperature = ...°C

[2]

ii) State and explain the process by which thermal energy transfer from the heater to the block takes place.

....

....

....

....

[3]

c) The insulation used around the block is cotton wool. Cotton wool is a poor conductor. Explain how wrapping the block in cotton wool helps to reduce unwanted energy transfer away from the block while it is being heated.

....

....

....

....

....

[3]

[Total 13 marks]

4   A planet is orbiting a star. Radiation from the star is incident on the surface of the planet's atmosphere. The star transfers 400 J of energy per second to each square metre of the planet's atmosphere. The diagram below shows the paths taken by the incident radiation when it reaches the planet.

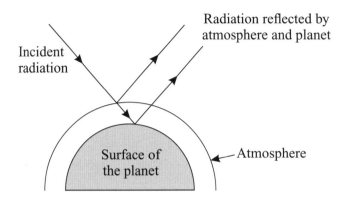

Of the radiation incident on the atmosphere 10% is reflected back into space and 20% is absorbed by the atmosphere. The rest of the radiation passes through the atmosphere to the surface of the planet. The radiation that reaches the surface of the planet is either reflected or absorbed. The ratio of radiation absorbed by the surface of the planet to the radiation reflected by the planet is 5:2.

You may assume that each unit of radiation transfers the same amount of energy, and any energy radiated from the atmosphere towards the surface of the planet is negligible.

a)   Calculate the amount of energy absorbed by 1 m² of the surface of the planet each second.

Energy = ... J

[2]

b)   A moon that orbits the planet passes between the star and the planet, causing an eclipse. Suggest the effect this will have on the surface temperature of the planet. Explain your answer.

....

....

....

....

[2]

[Total 4 marks]

Paper 2

Exam Practice Tip

Don't be surprised if you can't always just plug the numbers you've been given in a question into equations you've learnt. You might need to think about what you know about mathematical relationships in general to get to the answer, or at least to get the data into a form you can use.

Score:

30

Energy Resources

1 The residents of a village wants to start generating all their own electricity using a renewable resource. There is a fast-flowing stream near the village, in which they are considering installing a turbine and generator to produce electricity hydroelectrically. Their other options are to install wind turbines at a suitable site in the village or solar panels on the roofs of their houses.

The residents measure the wind speeds at a potential wind turbine site in the village. The histogram on the right shows the distribution of wind speeds at the site during one week.

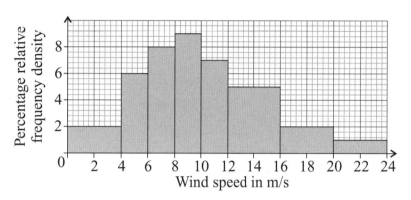

a) Calculate the percentage of time for which the wind speed was greater than 10 m/s.

Percentage time = ... %

[2]

The graph shows the typical power requirements of the village over a period of 24 hours.

b) Suggest which of the three options, hydroelectric, wind or solar power, is most likely to allow the residents to meet their energy needs.
You should explain your answer using information from the energy usage graph.

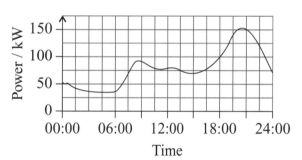

....

....

....

....

....

....

....

....

[6]

[Total 8 marks]

Score:

8

Paper 2

Density

1   Aerogels are synthetic solids with an extremely low density.

A company produces an aerogel with a density of 1.50 kg/m³. The diagram shows a block of the aerogel floating in some water. The aerogel has a mass of 0.50 kg. The volume of the aerogel below the waterline is 5×10^{-4} m³.

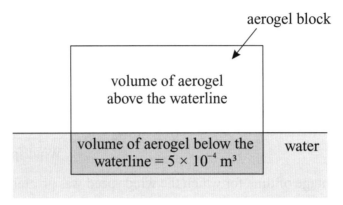

Not to scale

a)   Calculate the percentage of the volume of the aerogel that is below the waterline.

Percentage = ... %

[4]

b)   The company can make 0.360 m³ of the aerogel in 24 hours.
     Calculate the average rate of production of the aerogel. Give your answer in grams per minute.

Rate of production = ... g/min

[5]

[Total 9 marks]

Exam Practice Tip

If you're not sure where to start with a problem, try checking the units given in the answer — sometimes they'll offer clues about how the answer is calculated. For example, if it's a mass unit over a volume unit, you'll probably need to divide a mass by a volume.

Score: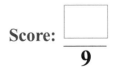

9

Specific Heat Capacity and Changes of State

1   Ball A is a 50 g ball made of aluminium. Ball A is heated and then
plunged into 1.0 kg of water that has an initial temperature of 27 °C.
The water and the ball eventually reach the same temperature of 30 °C.

a)   Calculate the temperature of ball A just before it was plunged into the water.
Assume no energy is lost to the surroundings. The specific heat capacity of water is 4200 J/kg°C.
The specific heat capacity of aluminium is 900 J/kg°C.

Temperature = ... °C

[5]

b)   Ball A is removed from the water and then heated at a constant rate for 45 minutes.
The temperature-time graph for ball A as it is being heated is shown.

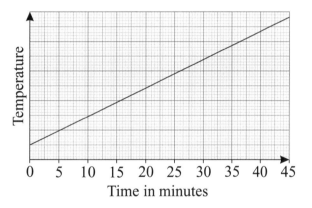

Time in minutes

Ball B is another aluminium ball. Ball B has half the mass
of ball A and has the same initial temperature as ball A.
On the graph, draw the temperature-time graph of ball B that would be produced
if energy was transferred to it at the same rate as ball A. Explain your answer.

....

....

....

....

....

....

[3]

[Total 8 marks]

Paper 2

2 The table below shows the specific heat capacities of different substances.

Substance	Specific heat capacity in J/kg°C
Tin	217
Ammonia (liquid)	4700
Ammonia (gas)	2060

An electric heater is used to transfer energy to different substances. It is assumed that no energy is wasted to the surroundings and no energy is transferred from the surroundings to the substances.

a) The heater is used to transfer 740 J of energy to a piece of tin.
The temperature of the tin increases by 30 °C.
Calculate the mass of this piece of tin. Give your answer to two significant figures.

Mass = ... kg
[4]

b) The heater continues to heat the tin at a constant rate.
Once the tin reaches a certain temperature, the temperature of the tin stops changing.
Explain why.

....

....

....
[2]

c) The heater is then used to heat 30 g of ammonia. The ammonia is initially a liquid with a temperature of –60 °C. The ammonia boils at a temperature of –33 °C and then its temperature rises to –10 °C. The heater supplies a total of 46.3 kJ of energy to the ammonia during this time.

Calculate the energy that is used to change the state of the ammonia.
Give your answer to three significant figures.

Energy = ... J
[5]

[Total 11 marks]

Score: [   ]

19

Particle Motion in Gases

1   The graph below shows the relationship between depth underwater and pressure.

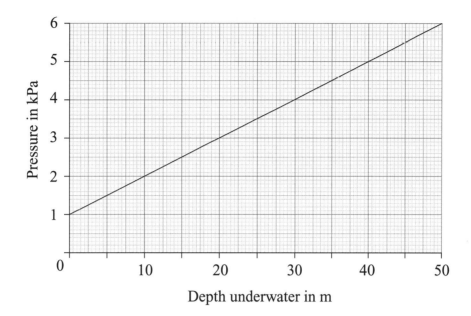

a) A diver notices that underwater air bubbles increase in size as they rise up.
Explain why this happens. Assume the temperature of the gas inside the bubbles stays constant.

....

....

....

....

....
[2]

b) A bubble produced underwater at a depth of 25 m moves upwards. By the time the
bubble reaches 10 m below the surface, it has expanded to a volume of 1000 cm³.
Use the graph to calculate the volume of the bubble at a depth of 25 m.
Assume the bubble maintains a constant temperature as it travels upwards.
Give your answer to two significant figures.

Volume = ... cm³
[4]

[Total 6 marks]

Section 5 — Solids, Liquids and Gases

2 An oxygen cylinder is shown below. Oxygen cylinders are rigid metal containers in which oxygen is stored. They are sometimes used by climbers at the top of mountains.

a) Use your knowledge of gas molecules to explain why the pressure inside an oxygen cylinder decreases as oxygen is removed from it.

....
....
....
....
....
....

[3]

b) A climber carries an oxygen cylinder up a mountain. The temperature decreases as the climber gets higher up the mountain. Explain how the pressure in the oxygen cylinder changes as it is carried up the mountain.

....
....
....
....
....
....
....
....

[4]

[Total 7 marks]

Exam Practice Tip

Sometimes an exam question might not give you the exact information you need to substitute into a formula. Those pesky examiners will make you work for it instead. If you are given something like a graph or a table, chances are you'll need to use it and it isn't just there to pretty up the page.

Score:

13

Section 5 — Solids, Liquids and Gases

Pressure

1   A jug containing water has oil poured into it.
The oil collects on the surface of the water, as
shown in the diagram. The layer of oil is 2 cm thick.

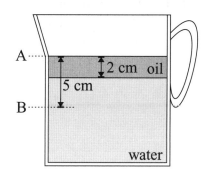

The difference in pressure between point A, at the surface of the
oil, and point B, 5 cm below the surface of the oil, is 470.4 Pa.
The density of water is 1000 kg/m³.

a) Calculate the density of the oil.
Gravitational field strength = 10 N/kg.

Density = ... kg/m³

[5]

b) Below is the first part of a graph showing how the pressure changes with depth below
the surface of the oil. The dotted line shows the boundary between the oil and water.
Complete the graph to show how the pressure may change as depth in the water continues to
increase. Explain your answer.

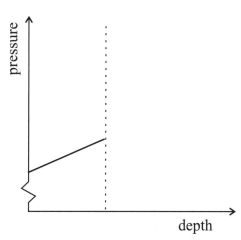

....

....

....

....

....

[3]

[Total 8 marks]

Section 5 — Solids, Liquids and Gases

2   An aerosol can is at 293 K. The internal pressure due to the compressed gas in it is 510 kPa.

a) The aerosol can has height, $h = 20$ cm and radius, $r = 2.5$ cm.
Calculate the total force exerted on the inside walls of the aerosol can by the compressed gas.
Give your answer to three significant figures.
Surface area of a cylinder $= 2\pi r(r + h)$. The aerosol can can be assumed to be a perfect cylinder.

Force = ... N

[5]

b) The density of water is 1000 kg/m³
Calculate the depth in water at which the pressure due to the water is equal to
the pressure inside the can. The gravitational field strength is 10 N/kg.

Depth = ... m

[3]

c) The aerosol can is heated, causing 1.1 kJ of energy to be transferred to the gas inside the can.
The mass of the gas is 200 g and the specific heat capacity of the gas is 620 J/kg K.
Calculate the new pressure of the compressed gas.

Paper 2

Pressure = ... Pa

[4]

[Total 12 marks]

Exam Practice Tip

The trickiest calculation questions in an exam will often require you to use two equations — one to
calculate a variable that you need to plug into the other. The worst case scenario is that you'll have
to pull both of the equations out of your hat. If you get lucky, one might be on the equation sheet.

Score:

20

Electromagnetism

[6]

1   Before digital ammeters were invented, analogue ammeters were used instead.
Analogue ammeters are based on a device called a moving-coil galvanometer.
The basic design of a moving-coil galvanometer is shown below.

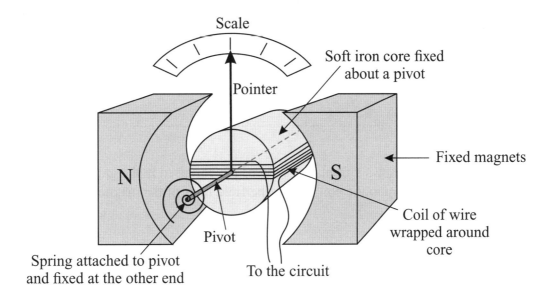

a) i) Explain how the moving-coil galvanometer could be used to detect a current in the circuit.
Include an explanation of what happens when the current is increased, removed and reversed.

....

....

....

....

....

....

....

....

....

....

....

....

[6]

34

The diagram below shows the magnetic field lines between
two flat magnets and two curved magnets.

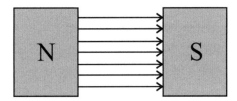 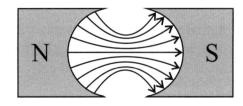

ii) Suggest why curved magnets are used for a moving-coil galvanometer. Explain your answer.

....

....

....

[2]

Paper 2

iii) The diagram below shows a front-end view of the coil used in the galvanometer and the
direction of the current in the coil. Draw the field lines of the magnetic field caused by the
current in the coil.

[2]

b) i) A student is building their own moving-coil galvanometer. They need to calibrate the scale so
that it reads the correct value when a current is applied. Suggest how they could do this.

....

....

[1]

ii) When the student tries to measure a larger current, the pointer moves off the end of the scale.
State **two** changes the student could make to the equipment to allow the galvanometer to
measure larger currents on the same sized scale.

1. ....

2. ....

[2]

[Total 13 marks]

Exam Practice Tip

If you get a question asking you about an unfamiliar application, don't panic. Read it through carefully
and work out which ideas you actually need to apply — it'll always be stuff you know. Then make sure
you reference those key ideas in your answer, whilst also keeping sight of the question context.

Score:

13

Section 6 — Magnetism and Electromagnetism

Transformers and Loudspeakers

1 Transformers are used in the national grid and in domestic appliances.

a) i) A transformer used in the national grid has 60 000 turns of wire on the primary coil and 45 000 turns of wire on the secondary coil. The input current is 1.2 kA. Calculate the output current.

Current = ... A

[3]

ii) State **one** assumption you have made in a) i).

....

[1]

b) An engineer is developing a transformer for use in a domestic appliance.
The transformer has an output voltage of 6 V. How could the engineer modify the transformer to double the output voltage without changing the input voltage?

☐ **A** Only by doubling the number of turns on the primary coil.

☐ **B** Only by doubling the number of turns on the secondary coil.

☐ **C** By doubling the number of turns on the secondary coil and halving the number of turns on the primary coil.

☐ **D** By either doubling the number of turns on the secondary coil or halving the number of turns on the primary coil.

[1]

c) The primary and secondary coils of a transformer are typically connected by a soft iron core.
State and explain why this material is suitable for this application.

....

....

....

....

....

[4]

[Total 9 marks]

Paper 2

2 The diagram shows a magnet being moved into a coil of wire that is part of a complete circuit. A current is induced in the wire. The induced current generates a magnetic field around the coil.

Movement →

| S | N |

Coil of wire

a) State how moving the magnet in the same way more quickly would affect the size of the current induced in the coil.

....
[1]

b) The diagram below shows a cone attached to a coil of wire. This can be used as part of a simple intercom system to convert between sound waves and electrical signals.

i) Explain how the equipment shown can be used to convert sound waves into electrical signals.

Coil of wire wrapped
around hollow cylinder

Cone

....

....

....

....

....

....
[4]

ii) Describe how the strength of the electrical signal produced by a sound wave could be increased.

....

....

....
[2]

[Total 7 marks]

Exam Practice Tip

If you see a diagram that looks familiar from your revision, it's tempting to assume you know what the question's about and start dashing off your answer. But still read the question carefully — you don't want to be caught out by the diagram showing something slightly different to what you expect.

Score:

16

The Atomic Model and Nuclear Radiation

1 Part of the periodic table is shown below. It shows the symbol, name and atomic number of different elements.

Symbol:	K	Ca	Sc	Ti
Name:	potassium	calcium	scandium	titanium
Atomic number:	19	20	21	22
Symbol:	**Rb**	**Sr**	**Y**	**Zr**
Name:	rubidium	strontium	yttrium	zirconium
Atomic number:	37	38	39	40
Symbol:	**Cs**	**Ba**	**La**	**Hf**
Name:	caesium	barium	lanthanum	hafnium
Atomic number:	55	56	57	72

a) i) Yttrium-93 can undergo radioactive decay to form zirconium-93.
State the type of radioactive decay that yttrium-93 undergoes.

....
[1]

ii) Complete the nuclear equation for this decay of yttrium-93.

$$\frac{\ldots}{\ldots}\text{Y} \rightarrow \frac{\ldots}{\ldots}\text{Zr} + \frac{\ldots}{\ldots}\ldots$$

[2]

b) i) Caesium-112 decays by emitting a single particle to form iodine-108.
Explain the changes in the caesium nucleus for this decay.

....

....

....
[2]

ii) Using your answer to b) i), calculate the atomic number of iodine.

Atomic number = ...
[1]

c) Titanium is formed by fusion in stars.
Which element could form titanium by fusion with another element?

☐ **A** Calcium   ☐ **C** Strontium

☐ **B** Rubidium   ☐ **D** Caesium

[1]

d) The part of the periodic table shown doesn't give a value for the mass number of each element.
Suggest why this is not usually possible.

....
[1]

[Total 8 marks]

2   A village's water supply comes from a nearby lake. The lake has
     been contaminated with a nuclear material. The graph below
     shows how the count-rate measured in the lake changes over time.

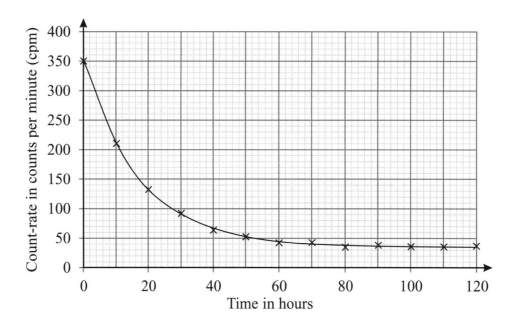

a) i) The count-rate measured was not corrected for background radiation.
        Estimate the background radiation count-rate.

                                Background radiation = ... cpm
                                                                                        [1]

   ii) Draw a line on the graph showing how the corrected count-rate changes over time.

                                                                                        [2]

b) Estimate the half-life of the sample.

                                Half-life = ... hours
                                                                                        [2]

c) i) The water is safe to drink when the corrected count-rate of the contaminated water falls below
        25 counts per minute. The decay curve was produced using data from a radiation detector
        which is accurate to ± 5 cpm. How many hours after the source of contamination has stopped
        will the water first become safe to drink? Explain your answer.

        ....

        ....

        ....
                                                                                        [2]

   ii) The water company won't declare contaminated water safe to drink until it has been below
        25 counts per minute for more than 24 hours. Suggest why this is the case.

        ....

        ....
                                                                                        [1]
                                                                              [Total 8 marks]

Section 7 — Radioactivity and Particles

3 Radiation can be used to check for cracks in metal turbine blades in jet engines, as shown below.

a) The blades are several centimetres thick.
Suggest what type of radiation the source should emit.

Radiation detector ←

Radiation source →

Jet turbine blade ←

....
[1]

b) Explain how the equipment in the diagram could be used to detect a crack in a turbine blade.

....

....

....

....
[3]

[Total 4 marks]

4 Radioactive isotopes are used as tracers in medical imaging.

a) i) The radioactive isotope iodine-131 has a half-life of 8.0 days. It is used as a medical tracer.
It is taken into the body and a detector outside the body traces its position. Iodine-131
undergoes beta decay and then gamma decay to form stable xenon (Xe).
Complete the two nuclear decay equations below to show these processes.

$$^{131}_{\ldots}\text{I} \rightarrow \, ^{\ldots}_{54}\text{Xe} + \, ^{\ldots}_{\ldots}\text{e} \qquad\qquad ^{\ldots}_{54}\text{Xe} \rightarrow \, ^{\ldots}_{\ldots}\text{Xe} + \, ^{\ldots}_{\ldots}\gamma$$

[2]

ii) Give **two** reasons why iodine-131 is a suitable radioactive isotope to be used as a medical tracer.

1. ....

....

2. ....

....
[2]

b) Iodine-131 can be used in radioiodine therapy to treat thyroid cancer. Iodine-131 capsules are
taken by the patient and the isotope travels to the thyroid where it kills cancer cells with radiation.
Suggest why patients often have to stay in hospital and why there are strict limitations on visitors.

....

....

....
[2]

[Total 6 marks]

Exam Practice Tip

A lot of this section comes back to understanding the different types of decay. Once you know the
properties of alpha, beta and gamma decay you can apply that knowledge to all sorts of questions
about nuclear equations, irradiation, contamination, uses of radiation and so on.

Score:

26

Fission and Fusion

1   Uranium-235 is a radioactive material used as fuel in fission reactors. It releases both gamma rays and alpha particles as part of the decay process. Workers at nuclear power stations wear protective suits, as shown below, when working with uranium-235.

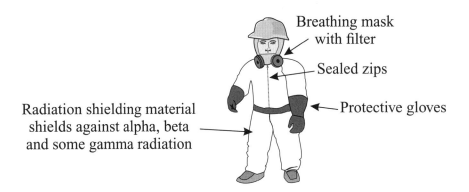

a)   Describe the risks of contamination and irradiation from the different types of radiation emitted by uranium-235. Explain how the design of the protective suit shown protects the user from contamination and radiation.

....

....

....

....

....

....

....

....

....

....

[4]

b)   Uranium-235 undergoes nuclear fission in a nuclear reactor. Which decay equation shows the nuclear fission of uranium-235 in a nuclear chain reaction?

☐   **A** $^{235}_{92}U + ^{1}_{0}n \rightarrow ^{92}_{36}Kr + ^{144}_{56}Ba$

☐   **B** $^{235}_{92}U \rightarrow ^{92}_{36}Kr + ^{141}_{56}Ba + 2^{1}_{0}n$

☐   **C** $^{235}_{92}U + ^{1}_{0}n \rightarrow ^{92}_{36}Kr + ^{141}_{56}Ba + 3^{1}_{0}n$

☐   **D** $^{235}_{92}U + ^{235}_{92}U \rightarrow 2^{92}_{36}Kr + ^{141}_{56}Ba + ^{144}_{56}Ba + ^{1}_{0}n$

[1]

[Total 5 marks]

2   A boiling water nuclear reactor is shown in the diagram below.

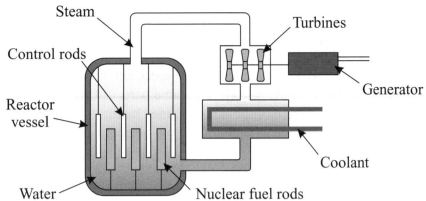

a) In a nuclear reactor, the nuclear fuel rods generate a huge amount of energy which heats the water surrounding the fuel rods. As the water is heated it boils and turns into steam. The steam rises and turns the turbines, generating electricity in the generator.
Which of the following increases the energy produced by a nuclear reactor?

☐   **A**   Cooling the steam before it reaches the turbines.

☐   **B**   Increasing the boiling point of the water in the reactor.

☐   **C**   Increasing the number of secondary fissions caused
by each fission in the chain reaction.

☐   **D**   Adding more neutron-absorbing control rods.

[1]

b) A beta-emitting radioactive isotope called iodine-131 is often released into the air during nuclear accidents. It can settle on skin and clothing and can be inhaled or ingested. Iodine is absorbed in the body by the thyroid gland, where it is used to make molecules that travel throughout the body. When the thyroid gland has enough iodine, any excess iodine is removed by the body. If a nuclear accident occurs at a power plant, workers are asked to ingest potassium iodide tablets which contain a stable isotope of iodine. Explain how this minimises the risk of damage to their bodies.

....

....

....

....

....

....

[4]
[Total 5 marks]

Exam Practice Tip

A question might give you a lot of written information and then ask you to explain something relating to it. In your answer you should make sure to use the information given, but without just repeating it — you'll need to apply your scientific reasoning to figure out how it all fits together.

Score: ☐
10

 ☐   ☐   ☺ ☐

Astrophysics

1   An astronomer is investigating the visible light from a distant galaxy, galaxy X.
She splits the light observed into a continuous spectrum, known as an absorption spectrum.

In an absorption spectrum, dark lines appear in the spectrum, corresponding to wavelengths
of light absorbed by elements in the galaxy. The same parts of two spectra are shown below.
Spectrum A is part of the spectrum of the light obtained by the astronomer on Earth.
Spectrum B is part of the spectrum of light that would be obtained if it was detected immediately
after it was emitted from galaxy X.

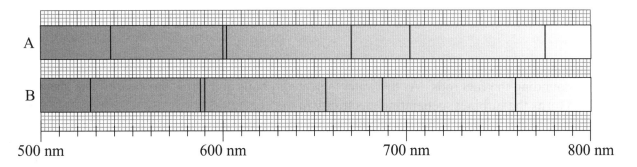

500 nm   600 nm   700 nm   800 nm

The astronomer observes that the absorption spectra have the same pattern of dark lines,
but that this pattern has been shifted by the time it reaches the Earth. This is red-shift.

a) i) Explain how the behaviour of the universe caused the light from the galaxy to be red-shifted.

....

....

....

....
[2]

The red-shift of a galaxy, z, can be calculated using the equation:

$$z = \frac{\Delta\lambda}{\lambda}$$

Where: λ = the wavelength of a dark line in absorption spectrum B
    $\Delta\lambda$ = the difference between λ and the wavelength of the equivalent dark line in
        absorption spectrum A

ii) Calculate the red-shift of galaxy X.
    Give your answer to two significant figures.

Red-shift = ...
[4]

Galaxy Y is even further away from Earth than galaxy X. The astronomer knows that, at the point of emission, galaxy Y has an identical absorption spectrum to galaxy X.

She compares the visible light absorption spectrum detected on Earth from galaxy Y with spectrum B. She finds that the absorption lines with the longest wavelengths are missing.

b) Explain why the absorption lines are missing from the visible part of the spectrum. Suggest what the astronomer could do to observe the missing absorption lines.

....

....

....

....

....

....

[3]

[Total 9 marks]

2   Star A and star B are main sequence stars with masses similar to that of the Sun.
The positions of star A and star B on the Hertzsprung-Russell diagram are shown below.

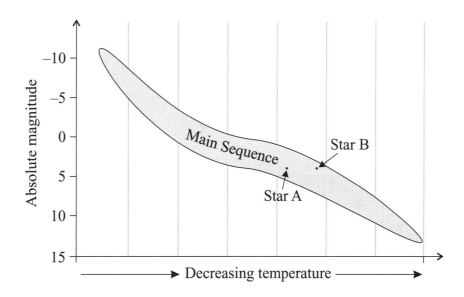

a) i)   Draw an arrow to show where on the Hertzsprung-Russell diagram star A will move to when it evolves into a white dwarf.

[1]

ii)   From Earth, star B appears brighter than star A in the night sky.
Explain how this is possible when both stars have the same absolute magnitude.

....

....

....

[2]

Section 8 — Astrophysics

b) Star B is orbited by a planet, planet C.

   i) It takes planet C 250 days to complete its circular orbit, travelling at an orbital speed of 36 km/s. Calculate the orbital radius of planet C's orbit.

Orbital radius = ... m

[3]

   ii) Planet C has a moon. The orbital speed of planet C's moon is 815 m/s. The circumference of the moon's circular orbit around planet C is 3.52×10^9 m. Calculate how many times the moon orbits planet C during one complete orbit of planet C around star B. Give your answer to the nearest whole number.

Number of orbits = ...

[4]

[Total 10 marks]

---

3   The visible absorption spectra for two distant galaxies, galaxy P and galaxy Q, are shown below.

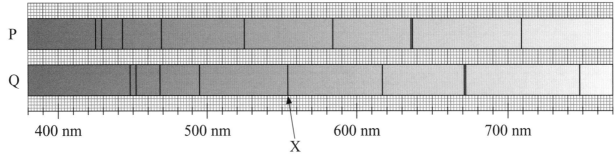

a) The line marked X in the spectrum of galaxy Q is produced by the absorption of light by hydrogen atoms. When the absorption spectrum of hydrogen gas on Earth is recorded, this line appears at a wavelength of 486 nm.

   i) State and explain which of the galaxies, P or Q, has the greater velocity relative to Earth.

....

....

....

[1]

Section 8 — Astrophysics

ii) Calculate the velocity at which galaxy Q is moving away from the Earth.
The speed of light in free space, $c = 3.0 \times 10^8$ m/s.

Velocity = ... m/s

[4]

The red-shift of light received on Earth from distant galaxies is
one piece of evidence that supports the Big Bang theory.

b) Describe **one** other piece of evidence that supports the Big Bang theory.
Explain how this piece of evidence supports the Big Bang theory.

....

....

....

....

....

....

[3]

c) Galaxy R is a nearby galaxy that is moving towards the Earth.

State and explain how you would expect the absorption spectrum of visible light observed from
this galaxy to compare to an absorption spectrum caused by the same elements on Earth.

....

....

....

....

[2]

[Total 10 marks]

Paper 2

Section 8 — Astrophysics

Mixed Questions for Paper 1

1   The two graphs below illustrate how the thinking distance and braking distance of a moving car vary with the speed of the car in good driving conditions.

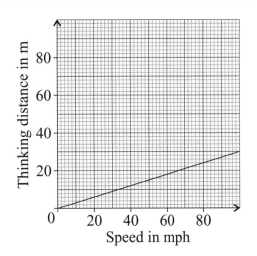

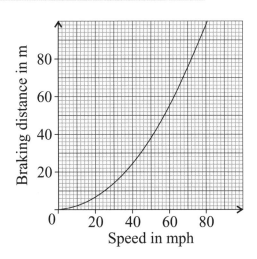

a) When the brakes are applied, they do work to transfer energy away from the kinetic energy store of the car.
    Explain the shapes of the graphs shown.
    In your answer you should refer to relevant equations of motion and energy transfers.

    ....

    ....

    ....

    ....

    ....

    ....

    ....

    ....

    ....

    ....

    ....
                                                                                                                                              [5]

b) Estimate the stopping distance of a car when it is travelling at 33 m/s.
    1 mph = 0.447 m/s.

    Stopping distance = ... m
                                                                                                                                              [3]

c) Explain how the two graphs would be different for driving conditions where the road is slippery.

....

....

....

....

....

....

[4]

[Total 12 marks]

2   The diagram below shows a train's emergency brake system. The driver of the train spots a hazard and pushes a button that triggers the emergency brake.

a) The coil and brake plate are mounted on the train above the rails and can move up or down. When the driver presses the button, the switch closes.
Explain how pressing the button causes the train to come to a stop.

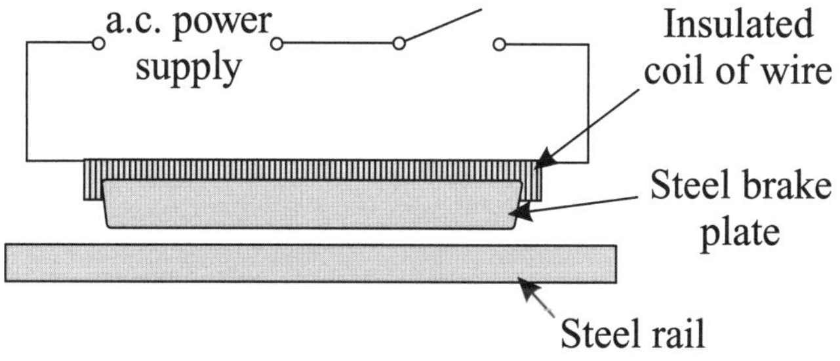

a.c. power supply

Insulated coil of wire

Steel brake plate

Steel rail

....

....

....

....

....

....

[4]

b) The train has a mass of 200 000 kg and is travelling at 28 m/s on a level track before the button is pressed. The emergency brakes provide a constant resultant force of 0.4 MN on the train. Calculate the braking distance of the train.

Braking distance = ... m

[5]

[Total 9 marks]

Mixed Questions for Paper 1

3   A boy skims a stone across a lake. The velocity-time graph for the vertical component of the stone's velocity from the time it first touches the water is shown below.

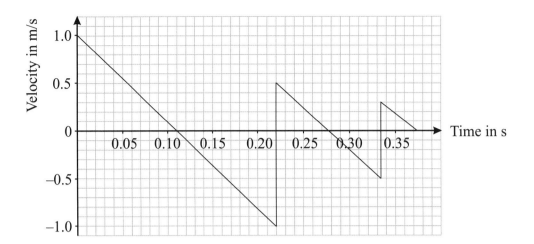

a) i) Describe the motion of the stone between 0.11 s and 0.22 s.

....

....

[2]

ii) Determine the maximum height the stone reached after first touching the water.

Height = ... m

[2]

b) The stone settles on the lake floor. Light travels through water more slowly than it travels through air. Complete the diagram below to show the ray of light from the Sun reflecting from the stone and back out of the water.

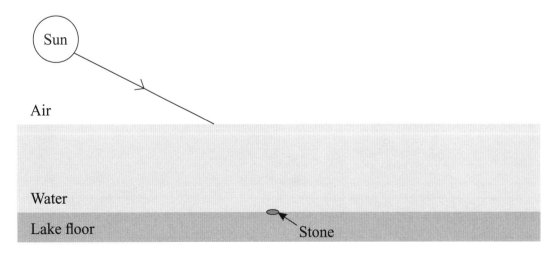

[2]

[Total 6 marks]

Mixed Questions for Paper 1

4 A skyscraper has a total height of 300 m.

a) A lift inside the skyscraper carries tourists to the top. The lift has a mass of 1200 kg.
The maximum mass that the tourist lift can carry in addition to its own weight is 700 kg.
The energy the lift uses to travel the full 300 m to the top of the building at full capacity is 9500 kJ.
Calculate the efficiency of the lift at full capacity. The gravitational field strength is 10 N/kg.

Efficiency = ... %

[4]

b) The lift is fitted with a 75 W light bulb. The potential difference
across the light bulb is 120 V. Calculate the resistance of the light bulb.

Resistance = ... Ω

[5]

c) A coin is dropped from the top of the building. It falls 300 m to the ground.
Calculate the speed of the coin just before it hits the ground.
State any assumptions you make.

Speed = ... m/s

[5]

[Total 14 marks]

5 When some stars explode, they leave behind a very dense object called a neutron star.

a) A neutron star has a mass of 2.1×10^{30} kg and a volume of 1.4×10^{13} m³. A sugar cube has a
volume of 1.0×10^{-6} m³. Calculate how much mass a sugar cube with the same density as this
neutron star would have.

Mass = ... kg

[5]

Mixed Questions for Paper 1

b) It is thought that the core of a neutron star consists of neutrons that are closely packed together. Explain, using the nuclear model of the atom, why solid matter found on Earth is much less dense than neutron star matter.

....

....

....

[2]

c) The Sun releases approximately 4×10^{26} J of energy per second. The kind of explosions that produce neutron stars can release as much as 1×10^{44} J of energy. Calculate how many years it would take for the Sun to release this amount of energy if it continued releasing energy at the same rate. Give your answer to one significant figure.

Time taken = ... years

[3]

d) Every star starts its life as a gas cloud. Explain how the pressure in the gas cloud changes if the cloud is heated by a nearby star, assuming the gas cloud has a constant volume.

....

....

....

....

[3]

e) i) Name the process by which stars such as the Sun release energy.

....

[1]

ii) Explain why this process cannot take place in the gas cloud.
You should use ideas about particles and the forces between them in your answer.

....

....

....

....

[3]

[Total 17 marks]

Exam Practice Tip

Think carefully about the questions in this mixed topic — they might seem to be asking about one topic, but actually need information from another. You might need to draw together your knowledge from different areas of the course, so bear that in mind if you get stuck.

Score:

58

Mixed Questions for Paper 1

Mixed Questions for Paper 2

1   The diagram shows a golf club hitting a stationary golf ball of mass 45 g.

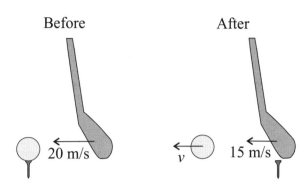

Before   After

20 m/s   v   15 m/s

The club has a mass of 0.40 kg and travels at 20 m/s before hitting the ball. Immediately after hitting the ball, the club slows down to 15 m/s.

a) i)   Calculate the size of the velocity of the ball immediately after it has been hit.
Give your answer to two significant figures.

Velocity = ... m/s
[5]

ii)   The ball lands on level ground, then rolls along the ground for 5 s before coming to a stop.
The initial velocity of the ball after landing on the ground is 3 m/s.
Calculate the size of the average resistive force acting on the ball as it rolls along the ground.

Force = ... N
[4]

b)   The same golf club is used to hit a second golf ball, also with a mass of 45 g. This new golf ball is designed so that when it's hit by the club, there is a longer contact time compared to the first ball. Assuming that both balls experience the same average force whilst in contact with the club, explain how the balls' velocities will differ immediately after being hit.

....

....

....

....

[2]

[Total 11 marks]

2 In the 1600s, Johannes Kepler developed a series of laws for how the planets of the solar system orbit the Sun. These are known as Kepler's laws of planetary motion.

a) The planets orbit the Sun in almost circular orbits. Explain how, as a planet orbits the Sun, it can be constantly accelerating while its speed remains constant.

....

....

....

....

[2]

Kepler's Third Law states:

$$T^2 = k \times r^3$$

Where: T = time taken for a full orbit (the orbital period) in s
k = a constant known as Kepler's constant in s^2/m^3
r = distance from the orbiting object to the object it is orbiting in m

Kepler's Third Law can also be applied to the orbits of moons around planets and dwarf planets. The table below shows data about some of Pluto's moons.

Moon	Distance from Pluto (m)	(Distance from Pluto)^3 (m^3)	Orbital period (s)	(Orbital period)^2 (s^2)
Styx	42.4×10^6	7.62×10^{22}	1.74×10^6	3.03×10^{12}
Nix	48.7×10^6	1.16×10^{23}	2.15×10^6	4.62×10^{12}
Kerberos	57.8×10^6	1.93×10^{23}	2.78×10^6	7.73×10^{12}
Hydra	64.7×10^6	2.71×10^{23}	3.30×10^6	1.09×10^{13}

An incomplete graph of the square of the orbital period of the moons against the cube of their distance from Pluto is shown below.

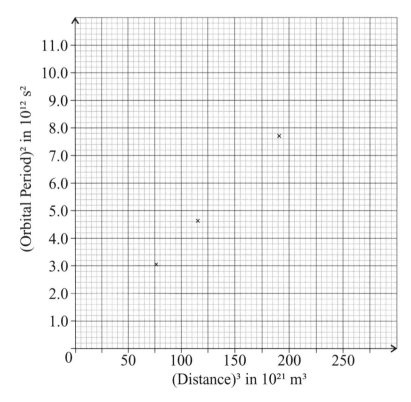

b) i) Complete the graph by plotting the missing point for Hydra. Draw a line of best fit.

[2]

    ii) Calculate Kepler's constant for objects orbiting Pluto.

Kepler's constant = ... s^2/m^3

[2]

c) A scientist is using a radio telescope to observe Pluto. When she orientates the telescope in any direction away from Pluto, she detects microwave radiation at a frequency of 160 GHz. Explain the origin of this radiation and what it indicates about the beginning of the universe.

....

....

....

....

....

[3]

[Total 9 marks]

3   Substations are a part of the national grid. They contain a number of electrical devices that are used to adjust the mains electricity supply before it reaches consumers.

a) The electricity transferred to a device in a substation has a power of 1.843 GW. Once passed through the device, the electricity has a current of 166 kA. The power of the electricity coming out of the device is 99% of the power supplied to the device. Calculate the voltage of the electricity after it has passed through the device. Give your answer to three significant figures.

Voltage = ... V

[5]

b) A humming sound can sometimes be heard coming from the high voltage cables near the substation. This sound has the same frequency as that of the a.c. electricity passing through the cables, 50 Hz. At times of high demand, the a.c. frequency may decrease slightly. Predict how this affects the humming sound heard. Explain your answer.

....

....

....

[2]

One of the cables near the substation breaks and comes into direct contact with the metal body of a car.

A current flows through the cable to the car for 0.55 s before the supply is cut off. The cable transfers electricity with a power of 0.31 GW.

c) The voltage between the cable and the car is 380 kV.
Calculate the total charge that is transferred to the car during the fault.

Charge = ... C

[5]

d) Explain how a car might gain an electric charge under normal conditions when it is travelling at high speeds.

....

....

[1]

[Total 13 marks]

4   A student is investigating the rate of cooling of different substances.

a) The student uses a 12 V immersion heater to heat 100 g of water in an insulated beaker.
    In 5 minutes, the temperature of the water increases from 25 °C to 61 °C.
    Calculate the current through the heater. The specific heat capacity of water is 4200 J/kg °C.
    You may assume that the transfer of energy from the heater to the water is 100%
    efficient, and that no energy is lost from the water to its surroundings in this time.

                                              Current = ... A
                                                                          [5]

b) The student removes the heater and the insulation from the beaker and leaves
    the water to cool down. Explain how the arrangement and motion of the
    particles in the water change as the temperature of the water decreases.

    ....

    ....

    ....

    ....
                                                                          [3]

The student records the temperature of the water every 100 seconds.
He produces the graph below to show how the temperature of the water changes over time.

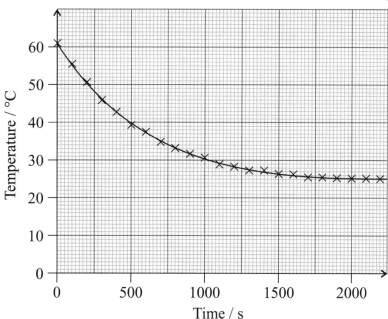

c) Determine the instantaneous rate of temperature change of
    the water 1000 s after the start of monitoring.

                              Rate of temperature change = ... °C/s
                                                                          [3]

56

d) The student also heats 100 g of olive oil to a temperature of 61 °C and then leaves it to cool. The equipment used and the conditions in the laboratory are identical to those used when heating and cooling the water. The specific heat capacity of olive oil is 1970 J/kg °C.

i) On the graph, sketch the cooling curve you predict the student will obtain for olive oil.

[2]

ii) Explain your prediction.

....

....

....

....

[3]

[Total 16 marks]

5   A mobile phone charger contains a transformer to decrease the mains potential difference to the potential difference needed to charge a phone battery. While being charged, the phone is attached to the secondary coil of the transformer as part of a charging circuit.

a) The primary coil of the transformer has 920 turns. The voltage across the primary coil is 230 V and the current through it is 40 mA. A current of 1840 mA is required in the charging circuit. Calculate the number of turns on the secondary coil, assuming the transformer is 100% efficient.

Number of turns = ...

[5]

b) Transformers work using electromagnetic induction.
Explain why transformers can only be used with an alternating voltage.

....

....

....

....

[3]

[Total 8 marks]

Exam Practice Tip

Well, that's it — you've made it to the end. I hope you've enjoyed stretching your physics muscles and now feel ready to take on the real exams. Make sure you rest up and get an early night before each exam so you're bright-eyed and bushy-tailed, ready to show that physics exam who's boss.

Score:

57

Mixed Questions for Paper 2

Answers

Section 1 — Forces and Motion

Pages 1-2: Forces and Moments

1 a)   Resultant force = upwards forces − downwards forces
$$= 40.0 \times 10^6 - (7.60 \times 10^6 + 9.40 \times 10^6)$$
$$= 23 \times 10^6 \text{ N}$$
So need to draw a 23 mm arrow pointing upwards, e.g.:

[1 mark for arrow drawn from the × and pointing directly upwards, 1 mark for the line being 23 mm in length]

b)   Find the gravitational field strength of the Earth's gravitational field at the Moon:
$$g = \frac{GM_E}{r^2} = \frac{(6.67 \times 10^{-11}) \times (5.97 \times 10^{24})}{(3.84 \times 10^8)^2} = 0.00270... \text{ N/kg}$$
$W = m \times g$
so $m = W \div g$
$m = 1.98 \times 10^{20} \div 0.00270...$
$= 7.3320... \times 10^{22}$
$= \mathbf{7.33 \times 10^{22} \text{ kg (to 3 s.f.)}}$

[5 marks for correct answer, otherwise 1 mark for correct substitution into gravitational field strength equation, 1 mark for correct calculation of gravitational field strength, 1 mark for correct rearrangement of weight equation and 1 mark for correct substitution into weight equation]

2 a)   Weight of the plank, $W_p = m_p \times g = 9.4 \times 10 = 94$ N

Weight of mass at B, $W_B = m_B \times g = 8.8 \times 10 = 88$ N

Since plank is uniform, weight of plank acts at centre, 3 m from support A.
The distance from support A to support C is twice the distance from C to D, so:
Distance AC = 4.0 m, Distance CD = 2.0 m,
Distance AB = Distance BC = 2.0 m
The weight of the plank acts at 1.0 m from point C.
Let the force applied by support A = F_A
Taking moments about point C, given that the plank is balanced:
clockwise moments = anticlockwise moments
$F_A \times 4.0 = (88 \times 2.0) + (94 \times 1.0)$
$$F_A = \frac{(88 \times 2.0) + (94 \times 1.0)}{4.0}$$
$= 67.5$ N
$= \mathbf{68 \text{ N (to 2 s.f.)}}$

[5 marks for correct answer, otherwise 1 mark for correct calculation of the weights of masses, 1 mark for equating the clockwise and anticlockwise moments about point C, 1 mark for correct substitution into this equation and 1 mark for correct rearrangement to find the force at point A]

b)   A *[1 mark]*
The mass is the same distance from both pivots, but the distance from point D to point C is shorter than that from point D to point A, and that from point A to point C. So the most force will be required to lift the mass by pressing down at point D and pivoting about point C.

Pages 3-4: Motion

1 a)   Total distance moved = 740 + 1400 + 360 = 2500 m
Average speed = 27.2 m/s
total distance moved = average speed × total time taken
so, total time taken = total distance moved ÷ average speed
$$= 2500 \div 27.2$$
$$= 91.9117... \text{ s}$$
Time taken for last 360 m = 91.9117... − 27 − 50
$$= 14.9117... \text{ s}$$
$$= \mathbf{14.9 \text{ s (to 3 s.f.)}}$$
[3 marks for correct answer, otherwise 1 mark for correct rearrangement of speed equation and 1 mark for correct substitution to find total time taken]

b)   Speed is the gradient of a distance-time graph. Maximum speed occurs at point when gradient is greatest, between around 252-264 s.
Draw a tangent at this point.
E.g.

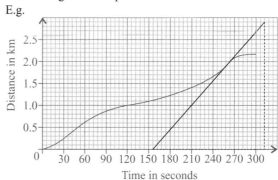

Find the gradient of the tangent:
change in y = 2.9 − 0 = 2.9 km
change in x = 312 − 156 = 156 s
$$\text{speed} = \text{gradient} = \frac{\text{change in } y}{\text{change in } x} = \frac{2.9}{156} = 0.01858... \text{ km/s}$$
To convert to km/h, multiply km/s by 60 × 60 = 3600
speed = 0.01858... × 3600
$$= 66.923...$$
$$= \mathbf{67 \text{ km/h (to 2 s.f.)}}$$
(Accept between 62 km/h and 72 km/h)
[5 marks for correct answer, otherwise 1 mark for suitable tangent drawn, 1 mark for attempt to calculate gradient, 1 mark for correct calculation of speed in km/s or m/s and 1 mark for correct unrounded answer]

)   C *[1 mark]*
The maximum speed is 9 m/s.
So the speed in knots is 9 ÷ 0.5 = 18.0 knots.

b)   average speed = total distance moved ÷ total time taken
Distance moved is given by area under graph.
Each square = 2 × (5 × 60) = 600 m
Number of squares under graph = 31.5
So, area under graph = 31.5 × 600 = 18 900 m
(Accept between 18 600 m and 19 200 m)
time = 50 minutes = 50 × 60 = 3000 s
So, average speed = 18 900 ÷ 3000
$$= \textbf{6.3 m/s}$$
(Accept between 6.2 m/s and 6.4 m/s)
[4 marks for correct answer, otherwise 1 mark for correct calculation of area of each square, 1 mark for multiplying area of one square by total number of squares and 1 mark for correct substitution into equation for speed]

Pages 5-7: More on Motion

1 a)   First find the final speed using the equation
$v^2 = u^2 + (2 \times a \times s)$
$v = \sqrt{u^2 + (2 \times a \times s)} = \sqrt{0.9^2 + (2 \times 10 \times 0.75)} =$
3.976... m/s
$a = \dfrac{v - u}{t}$
so $t = \dfrac{v - u}{a} = \dfrac{3.976... - 0.9}{10} = 0.307...$ s = **0.3 s (to 1 s.f.)**
[5 marks for correct answer, otherwise 1 mark for correct rearrangement of equation for final speed, 1 mark for correct substitution to find the final speed, 1 mark for correct calculation of final speed, 1 mark for correct substitution into equation to find time]

b)   The section of the graph that is a straight line with a positive gradient shows that the stone begins by accelerating downwards through the air at a constant rate, due to its weight *[1 mark]*.
Once the stone enters the water, upthrust and drag act against its motion, causing the rapid deceleration shown by the steep negative gradient *[1 mark]*.
The drag on the stone decreases as the stone's speed decreases, causing the stone's deceleration to decrease, so the graph becomes less steep *[1 mark]*.
Eventually the total upwards forces become equal to the weight of the stone *[1 mark]*.
At this point the acceleration of the stone becomes zero and the speed of the stone is constant, so the graph becomes a straight horizontal line *[1 mark]*.

2 a)   Mass is the ratio of force ÷ acceleration.
The gradient of the graph is acceleration ÷ force.
Therefore, mass = 1 ÷ gradient.
gradient $= \dfrac{4.0 - 0}{2.0 - 0}$
$= 2$
mass $= 1 \div 2$
$= \textbf{0.5 kg}$
[3 marks for correct answer, otherwise 1 mark for calculation of gradient and 1 mark for attempting to find the inverse of the gradient]

b)   Read correct acceleration from the line of best fit on the graph.
At 1.3 N, $a = 2.6$ m/s^2
$v^2 = u^2 + (2 \times a \times s)$, so:
$u = \sqrt{v^2 - (2 \times a \times s)}$
$= \sqrt{2.53^2 - (2 \times 2.6 \times 1)}$
$= 1.09585...$
$= \textbf{1.1 m/s (to 2 s.f.)}$
[5 marks for correct answer, otherwise 1 mark for correct value of acceleration from the line of best fit, 1 mark for correct rearrangement, 1 mark for correct substitution and 1 mark for correct unrounded answer]

c)   For the car to travel at a constant speed, the braking force must equal the force causing it to accelerate down the hill.
$F = m \times a$
Typical mass of a car ≈ 1000 kg
So, braking force $= 1000 \times 1.7$
$= \textbf{1700 N}$
[3 marks for correct answer, otherwise 1 mark for suitable typical mass of a car and 1 mark for correct substitution]
You'd get full marks here for correct calculations using any suitable value for the mass of a car.

3   The Earth exerts an attractive force on a person equal to their weight *[1 mark]*.
By Newton's third law, the person must exert an equal and opposite force on the Earth *[1 mark]*.
The Earth does not noticeably move towards the person because the Earth has a much higher mass than a person *[1 mark]* and since acceleration is inversely proportional to mass (Newton's second law) the Earth's acceleration towards the person is very small/negligible *[1 mark]*.

Answers

Pages 8-10: Stopping Distances and Momentum

1 a) i) First, calculate the final velocity of the ruler when it is caught.

$a = \dfrac{v - u}{t}$ so

$v - u = a \times t$

$\quad = 10 \times 0.21$

$\quad = 2.1$ m/s

As initial velocity = 0 m/s, the final velocity = 2.1 m/s.

Rearrange $v^2 = u^2 + (2 \times a \times s)$, for distance travelled:

$s = \dfrac{v^2 - u^2}{2a}$

$\quad = \dfrac{2.1^2 - 0^2}{2 \times 10}$

$\quad = 0.2205$ m

$\quad = 22.05$ cm

$\quad =$ **22 cm (to 2 s.f.)**

[5 marks for correct answer, otherwise 1 mark for correct calculation of the final velocity, 1 mark for correct rearrangement for distance travelled, 1 mark for correct substitution to find distance travelled and 1 mark for correct answer in m]

ii) Any two from: e.g. The ruler could be weighted at the bottom (e.g. with modelling clay) *[1 mark]*. This would ensure that the ruler falls vertically downwards, so distance measured is more accurate *[1 mark]*. / Another person should be present to make sure the ruler is aligned correctly with the thumb before being dropped *[1 mark]*. This will help prevent parallax errors in measuring the starting position of the ruler *[1 mark]*. / Several repeats should be taken and the average reaction time calculated *[1 mark]*. This will help reduce the effect of any random errors in the final result *[1 mark]*.

b) Person 3's reaction time is less than person 4's and so as the car's speed is the same for both people their thinking distance is shorter *[1 mark]*.
The braking distance is the same for both people, as all conditions relating to the car and road are the same *[1 mark]*, and so since stopping distance is the sum of thinking distance and braking distance, person 3 would be able to stop a car in the shorter distance *[1 mark]*

2 a) Conservation of momentum means that, as the total momentum before firing the rifle is zero, the total momentum after must also be zero *[1 mark]*.
Since the bullet has a momentum in one direction, the rifle must have a momentum in the opposite direction in order for the total momentum after to be zero, so the rifle must recoil *[1 mark]*.

b) E.g. increase the mass of the rifle *[1 mark]*.
Since momentum = mass × velocity, a larger mass will give a smaller velocity for a given momentum *[1 mark]*.

c) Let velocity to the right be positive.
For when the bullet is fired from the rifle:
momentum = mass × velocity
total initial momentum = 0 kgm/s *[1 mark]*
momentum of rifle after = 4.00 × −1.00
$\qquad\qquad\qquad\qquad = −4.00$ kgm/s
total momentum after = total momentum before
momentum of bullet after − 4.00 = 0 kgm/s
so momentum of bullet after = 4.00 kgm/s *[1 mark]*
For the collision between the bullet and the wooden block:
Momentum of bullet before = 4.00 kgm/s
Momentum of block before = 0.5 × 0
$\qquad\qquad\qquad\qquad = 0$ kgm/s
Momentum of block and bullet after = $(0.01 + 0.5) \times v_B$
Total momentum before = total momentum after
$4.00 = (0.01 + 0.5) \times v_B$ *[1 mark]*
$v_B = \dfrac{4.00}{0.51}$ *[1 mark]*
$\quad = 7.84313...$
$\quad =$ **7.84 m/s (to 3 s.f.)** *[1 mark]*

If you get the correct answer here, you'll get the full 5 marks, regardless of whether you've written down all the working shown above.

d) The deformable pad increases the time over which the rifle comes to rest after recoiling (by being compressed) *[1 mark]*.
Since force is equal to the rate of change of momentum $(F = (mv - mu)/t)$, this decreases the force on the shoulder *[1 mark]*, and so decreases the risk of injury to the shoulder *[1 mark]*.

3 a) Force acting to decelerate the car = −9570 N
$F = m \times a$,
so $a = F \div m$
$a = −9570 \div 1450$
$\quad = −6.6$ m/s^2
$v^2 = u^2 + (2 \times a \times s)$, so:
$s = \dfrac{v^2 - u^2}{2 \times a}$
$\quad = \dfrac{0^2 - 22.4^2}{2 \times −6.6}$
$\quad = 38.012...$ m
$\quad =$ **38.0 m (to 3 s.f.)**

[5 marks for correct answer, otherwise 1 mark for correct substitution into $F = m \times a$, 1 mark for correct calculation of deceleration, 1 mark for correct rearrangement of $v^2 = u^2 + (2 \times a \times s)$, 1 mark for correct substitution]

The energy transferred away from the car's kinetic energy store as it comes to rest is equal to the work done by the brakes. So you could also have done this question by saying that ½ × m × v^2 = F × d, from which you could work out the distance the car moved while the braking force was being applied.

b) Calculate the driver's reaction time:
$$\text{speed} = \frac{\text{distance moved}}{\text{time taken}} \text{ so}$$
$$\frac{\text{distance moved}}{\text{speed}}$$
$$\text{time taken} = \frac{14.6}{22.4}$$
$$= 0.6517...$$
Use the car's deceleration (calculated in a)) to calculate the time over which the braking force brings the car to rest:
$$a = \frac{(v-u)}{t} \text{ so}$$
$$t = \frac{(v-u)}{a} = \frac{(0-22.4)}{-6.6} = 3.3939...$$
$$\text{total time} = 0.6517... + 3.3939...$$
$$= 4.0457...$$
$$= \textbf{4.05 s (to 3 s.f.)}$$
[5 marks for correct answer, otherwise 1 mark for correct substitution into speed equation, 1 mark for correct calculation of reaction time, 1 mark for correct rearrangement of acceleration equation, 1 mark for correct substitution into acceleration equation]

You could also have found the time taken to brake using the equation for the average braking force: $F = \frac{mv - mu}{t}$. If you did it this way, you get 1 mark for rearranging the force equation and 1 mark for correctly substituting into it.

c) The time taken to bring the car to rest after the brakes are applied can be found using the equation $F = \frac{mv - mu}{t}$. The final velocity, v, is zero, and so doubling the initial velocity, u, would double the change in momentum $(mv - mu)$ *[1 mark]*.
For the braking force, F, to remain the same, the time taken would therefore also need to double, and so the student's hypothesis is incorrect *[1 mark]*.

Section 2 — Electricity

Pages 11-14: Circuits

1 a) $Q = I \times t$
$t = 2.0$ hours
$= 2.0 \times 60 \times 60$
$= 7200$ s
$Q = 0.50 \times 7200$
$= 3600$ C
Divide the total charge that passes through the thermistor by the charge on one electron to find the number of electrons:
$$\text{Number of electrons} = \frac{3600}{1.6 \times 10^{-19}}$$
$$= \textbf{2.25} \times \textbf{10}^{\textbf{22}}$$
[3 marks for correct answer, otherwise 1 mark for correct substitution into $Q = I \times t$ and 1 mark for dividing the total charge by the charge of an electron]

b) Find the potential difference across the resistor, V_2, and use this to find the current in the circuit:
$V_2 = V_{\text{total}} - V_1$
$= 6 - 0.25$
$= 5.75$ V

$V = I \times R$, so:
$$I = \frac{V_2}{R_2}$$
$R = 1$ k$\Omega = 1000$ Ω
$$I = \frac{5.75}{1000}$$
$= 0.00575$ A
Use the current in the circuit and V_1 to find the resistance of the thermistor:
$$R_1 = \frac{V_1}{I}$$
$$= \frac{0.25}{0.00575}$$
$$= 43.478... \, \Omega$$
$$= \textbf{43.5 } \Omega \textbf{ (to 3 s.f.)}$$
[5 marks for correct answer, otherwise 1 mark for correct calculation of V_2, 1 mark for correct substitution to find current through circuit, 1 mark for correct calculation of current and 1 mark for correct substitution to find R_1]

c) Adding the LED will cause the current in the circuit to decrease *[1 mark]*.
As the components are connected in series, the total resistance of the circuit is the sum of their individual resistances, and so it increases when the LED is added *[1 mark]*.
Since the voltage remains the same and $V = I \times R$, the current must decrease *[1 mark]*.

2 a) i) Line of best fit is a straight line, so it has an equation of the form $y = mx + c$,
where $y = R$, $m = $ gradient, $x = L$, and $c = y$-intercept.
Line goes through origin, so $c = 0$.
$$m = \text{gradient} = \frac{\text{change in } y}{\text{change in } x}$$
E.g. $m = \frac{54 - 0}{5.4 - 0}$
$= 10$

So, equation of line is $R = 10 L$
[2 marks for correct answer, otherwise 1 mark for correct calculation of the gradient]

Make sure you calculate the gradient from changes in y and x that cover at least half of the line of best fit.

ii) Calculate resistance of length of wire:
$R = 10L$,
so $R = 10 \times 0.375$
$= 3.75 \ \Omega$
Calculate current through wire:
$V = 500$ mV $= 500 \times 0.001 = 0.5$ V
$V = I \times R$ so $I = V \div R$
$I = 0.5 \div 3.75$
$= 0.1333...$ A
$= \mathbf{0.133 \ A}$ **(to 3 s.f.)**
[5 marks for correct answer, otherwise 1 mark for correct calculation of resistance of wire, 1 mark for correct rearrangement of V = I × R, 1 mark for correct substitution to find current and 1 mark for correct unrounded answer]

Even if you got the answer to 2 a) i) wrong, you get full marks for 2 a) ii) if you did the calculations correctly using your answer for 2 a) i).

b) From the graph: A 1.2 m length of the first wire, has a resistance of 12 Ω.
$R = \dfrac{k}{A}$
So $k = R \times A$
$= 12 \times 0.11$
$= 1.32$
For the second wire:
$R = \dfrac{1.32}{0.44}$
$= \mathbf{3.0 \ \Omega}$

[5 marks for correct answer, otherwise 1 mark for reading correct resistance value from graph, 1 mark for correct substitution into k = R × A, 1 mark for correctly calculating k, 1 mark for correct substitution into $R = \dfrac{k}{A}$]

You don't need to convert the areas to m^2 in this calculation. The equation shows that R ∝ 1/A, i.e. R and A are inversely proportional. So if A is multiplied by 4, R is divided by 4.

3 a) The total resistance of the circuit is equal to the sum of the resistances of the resistor and component X *[1 mark]*.
As voltage increases, the value of $\dfrac{V}{I}$ decreases (as shown by measuring V and I at points along the trend line and dividing the values), so the resistance of component X decreases *[1 mark]*.
The resistance of the resistor is constant, so as the voltage of the power supply increases, the total resistance of the circuit must decrease *[1 mark]*.

b) $E = I \times V \times t$, so $t = \dfrac{E}{I \times V}$
From the graph, when $V = 3.8$ V, $I = 1.8$ A.
1.0 kJ = 1000 J
$t = \dfrac{1000}{1.8 \times 3.8}$
$= 146.198...$ s
$= \mathbf{150 \ s}$ **(2 s.f.)**

[4 marks for correct answer, otherwise 1 mark for correct rearrangement of E = I × V × t, 1 mark for correctly reading current from graph, 1 mark for correct substitution into equation]

c) The amount of energy transferred per second will increase *[1 mark]*.

4 a) $E = Q \times V$
Energy transferred between 20 s and 30 s = 40 kJ − 20 kJ
$= 20$ kJ
$= 20\ 000$ J
$V = E \div Q$
$= 20\ 000 \div 12$
$= 1666.66...$ V
$= \mathbf{1700 \ V}$ **(to 2 s.f.)**
[5 marks for correct answer, otherwise 1 mark for correct energy values read from the graph, 1 mark for correct rearrangement, 1 mark for correct substitution and 1 mark for correct unrounded answer]

b) $V = I \times R$
$R = 250$ m$\Omega = 0.25 \ \Omega$
$V = 12 \times 0.25$
$= 3.0$ V
$P = I \times V$
$= 12 \times 3.0$
$= \mathbf{36 \ W}$

[4 marks for correct answer, otherwise 1 mark for correct substitution into V = I × R, 1 mark for correct calculation of the voltage, 1 mark for correct substitution into P = I × V]

Pages 15-16: Electrostatic Charges and Their Uses

1 a) i) The electrons being removed cause the paint droplets to have a positive charge *[1 mark]*. As all the droplets have a positive charge, they all repel one another and so spread out to produce a fine mist *[1 mark]*.
ii) $Q = I \times t$, so $I = Q \div t$
Total charge moving through the nozzle in one minute =
$Q = (1.9 \times 10^{-12}) \times (4.2 \times 10^{10})$
$= 0.0798$ C
$t = 1$ minute $= 60$ s
so $I = 0.0798 \div 60$
$= 0.00133$ A
$= \mathbf{0.0013 \ A}$ **(to 2 s.f.)**
[4 marks for correct answer, otherwise 1 mark for correct rearrangement of Q = I × t, 1 mark for correct calculation of total charge, 1 mark for correct substitution into I = Q ÷ t]

b) The positive paint droplets will be attracted to the object *[1 mark]* and repulsed by each other, causing the paint to spread out evenly over the object *[1 mark]*. Areas that have been painted become uncharged, ensuring that new paint only reaches unpainted areas and there is a uniform thickness of paint *[1 mark]*.

c) The operator should be earthed to prevent the build-up of excess static charge in their body*[1 mark]*, which could cause them to receive a shock/lead to sparks and a fire risk *[1 mark]*.

2 a) E.g. the image plate of the photocopier is positively charged *[1 mark]*. An image of the page is projected on to the image plate. Light hits the plate in the areas where the document is whiter and causes these areas to lose their charge *[1 mark]*. The areas that remain charged attract negatively charged black powder *[1 mark]*. This powder is then transferred on to positively charged paper, which is heated so the powder sticks and produces a copy of the original page *[1 mark]*.

b) Total energy transferred by the photocopier
= $(1.47 \times 10^3) \times 550 = 8.085 \times 10^5$ J
$E = Q \times V$, so:
$Q = E \div V$
$= 8.085 \times 10^5 \div 230$
$= 3515.217...$
= **3500 C (to 2 s.f.)**
[4 marks for correct answer, otherwise 1 mark for correct calculation of the total energy transferred, 1 mark for correct rearrangement of $E = Q \times V$, 1 mark for correct substitution]

c) Friction between the soles of the worker's shoes and the carpet causes electrons to move from one to the other, so that one becomes positively charged and the other negatively charged *[1 mark]*. The human body conducts charge, and so the charge spreads from the office worker's shoes into their body *[1 mark]*. When they touch the (metal) photocopier, the charge is conducted away, and so they experience a shock *[1 mark]*.

Section 3 — Waves

Page 17 — Properties of Waves

1 a) The distance between ten shadow lines is equal to nine wavelengths, so one wavelength, λ, is equal to
$\lambda = 27 \div 9$
$= 3$ cm
$= 0.03$ m
$f = 1 \div T$
$= 1 \div 0.25$
$= 4$ Hz
$v = f \times \lambda$
$= 4 \times 0.03$
= **0.12 m/s**
[5 marks for the correct answer, otherwise 1 mark for calculating the correct wavelength, 1 mark for correct substitution into $f = 1 \div T$, 1 mark for calculating the correct frequency and 1 mark for correct substitution into $v = f \times \lambda$]

b) The time interval is 0.25 s *[1 mark]*.
The time taken for a wave to travel exactly one wavelength ahead and take the place of the previous wave (and so appear to have not moved) is equal to the period of the wave *[1 mark]*.

Pages 18-20 — Wave Behaviour

1 a) The frequency of the sound heard by the observer is higher when the train is moving towards the observer *[1 mark]*. This is because the motion of the train causes the wavelength to become squashed *[1 mark]*. The frequency of the sound heard by the observer is lower when the train is moving away from the observer *[1 mark]*. This is because the motion of the train causes the observed (heard) wavelength to become longer than the wavelength emitted by the horn when stationary *[1 mark]*.

b) The greater the amplitude of the sheet's vibrations, the louder the sound it produces *[1 mark]*. The higher the frequency of the sheet's vibrations, the higher the pitch of the sound it produces *[1 mark]*.

c) E.g. Infrared radiation *[1 mark]*. An infrared sensor can detect body heat and so would be able to detect a intruder in the dark *[1 mark]*.

2 a) The light's wavelength will be reduced *[1 mark]*. Since $v = f \times \lambda$ and f is constant, a reduction in wave speed must lead to a reduction in wavelength *[1 mark]*.

b) The critical angle, c, of the block is given by:
$c = 100° \div 2$
$= 50°$
$\sin c = \dfrac{1}{n}$
$n = \dfrac{1}{\sin c}$
$= \dfrac{1}{\sin 50°}$
$= 1.305...$
= **1.31 (to 3 s.f.)**
[4 marks for the correct answer, otherwise 1 mark for correctly deducing the critical angle of the block, 1 mark for rearranging the critical angle equation for refractive index and 1 mark for correctly substituting into the equation]

c)

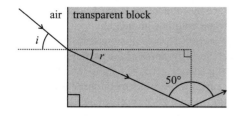

By considering the angles in a right-angled triangle, work out the angle of refraction, r:
$r + 50° = 90°$
$r = 90° - 50°$
$\quad = 40°$
$n = \dfrac{\sin i}{\sin r}$
$\sin i = n \sin r$
$\quad\quad = 1.305... \times \sin 40°$
$\quad\quad = 0.839...$
$i = \sin^{-1}(0.839...)$
$\quad = 57.0...°$
$\quad = \mathbf{57°}$ **(to 2 s.f.)**
[5 marks for the correct answer, otherwise 1 mark for correctly calculating the angle of refraction, 1 mark for correctly substituting into $\sin i = n \sin r$, 1 mark for correctly calculating the value of $\sin i$ and 1 mark for correctly rearranging for i]

You still get the marks here if the value for n that you calculated in part b) was incorrect, as long as you've carried out the right steps and got the correct answer for your value of n.

3 a)   E.g.

sound A

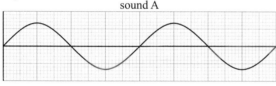

sound B

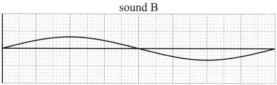

[1 mark for drawing A with a greater amplitude than B and 1 mark for drawing A with a shorter period than B]

b)   Lowest sound audible to the average human ~ 20 Hz.
This corresponds to a period of $\dfrac{1}{20} = 0.05$ s.
0.004 needs to be doubled 4 times in order to exceed 0.05s
$(0.004 \times 2 \times 2 \times 2 \times 2 = 0.064)$
So, the student must double the period of the signal produced by the signal generator 4 times before it becomes inaudible.
[3 marks for correct answer, otherwise 1 mark for recalling the lower frequency limit of human hearing and 1 mark for converting it into a period]

Since doubling the period halves the frequency, you could also have answered this question by converting the initial period to a frequency and then working out how many times the student would need to halve this frequency to bring it below 20 Hz.

Section 4 — Energy Resources and Energy Transfer

Pages 21-24 — Energy Transfers

1 a)   mass of stone, $m_s = 20$ g $= 0.02$ kg
mass of box $= 100$ g $= 0.1$ kg
total mass of box and stone, $m_T = 0.1 + 0.02 = 0.12$ kg
height of swing $= 20$ cm $= 0.2$ m
$\Delta GPE = m_T \times g \times \Delta h$
$\quad\quad\quad = 0.12 \times 10 \times 0.2$
$\quad\quad\quad = 0.24$ J
energy transferred to GPE stores of box and stone = energy transferred from kinetic energy store of the stone.
$\Delta GPE = KE = \frac{1}{2} \times m_s \times v^2$
$v = \sqrt{\dfrac{2 \times KE}{m_s}}$
$\quad = \sqrt{\dfrac{2 \times 0.24}{0.02}}$
$\quad = 4.8989...$ m/s
$\quad = \mathbf{4.9}$ **m/s (to 2 s.f.)**
[5 marks for correct answer, otherwise 1 mark for correct substitution into equation for gravitational potential energy, 1 mark for correct calculation of energy in gravitational potential energy store, 1 mark for correct rearrangement of the kinetic energy equation and 1 mark for correct substitution into the kinetic energy equation]

b)   E.g. as the box swings energy is dissipated to the thermal energy stores of the surroundings, reducing the energy in the gravitational potential energy store each time the swing peaks *[1 mark]*.

2 a)   Work is done to transfer energy to the kinetic energy store of the snooker ball. The amount of work done is equal to the amount of energy in the ball's kinetic energy store.
$KE = \frac{1}{2} \times m \times v^2$
$m = 140$ g $= 0.14$ kg
$KE = \frac{1}{2} \times 0.14 \times 1.6^2$
$\quad\quad = 0.1792$ J
$W = F \times d$, so $F = W \div d$
$d = 2.3$ mm $= 0.0023$ m
$F = 0.1792 \div 0.0023$
$\quad = 77.913...$ N
$\quad = \mathbf{78}$ **N (to 2 s.f.)**
[5 marks for correct answer, otherwise 1 mark for correct substitution into equation for kinetic energy, 1 mark for correct calculation of the energy in kinetic energy store, 1 mark for correct rearrangement of work done equation, 1 mark for correct substitution into work done equation]

b)   E.g. the balls are different temperatures because they are different colours *[1 mark]*. Overall, the black ball has absorbed more infrared radiation than the white ball *[1 mark]*.

3 a) Find the useful output energy transferred:
power = energy transferred ÷ time, so:
energy transferred = power × time
time = 9.0 × 60
= 540 s
power = 0.10 × 1000
= 100 W
useful energy output = 100 × 540
= 54 000 J
total energy output = useful energy output + wasted energy
= 54 000 + 300
= 54 300 J
efficiency = $\dfrac{\text{useful energy output}}{\text{total energy output}} \times 100\%$
= $\dfrac{54\,000}{54\,300} \times 100\%$
= 99.4475...%
= **99% (to 2 s.f.)**

[5 marks for correct answer, otherwise 1 mark for correct substitution into power equation, 1 mark for correct calculation of useful output energy transfer in 9 mins, 1 mark for correct calculation of total input energy transfer and 1 mark for correct substitution into efficiency equation]

b) i) Draw a line of best fit,
e.g.

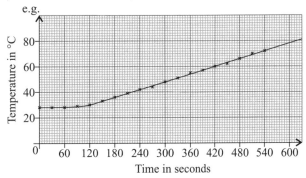

10 mins in seconds = 10 × 60
= 600 s
Evaluate temperature at 600 s,
Temperature = **78 °C**
(Accept between 76 °C and 80 °C)
[2 marks for correct answer, otherwise 1 mark for suitably drawn line of best fit with a constant positive gradient between 120 s and 600 s]

ii) Thermal energy transfer from the heater to the block takes place by conduction *[1 mark]*. Vibrating particles in the heater collide with neighbouring particles in the block *[1 mark]*. These collisions transfer energy from the kinetic energy stores of the particles in the heater to the kinetic energy stores of neighbouring particles in the block, causing a rise in temperature *[1 mark]*.

c) The cotton wool traps pockets of air close to the block, preventing convection currents from forming *[1 mark]*. So energy can only move away from the block by conducting through the cotton wool and the pockets of air *[1 mark]*, which is a very slow process due to the poor conducting properties of cotton wool and air *[1 mark]*.

4 a) 20% of the energy is absorbed by the atmosphere and 10% of the energy is reflected by the atmosphere, so 100 − 20 − 10 = 70% (or 0.7) is transmitted through.
Energy of radiation that is transmitted through the atmosphere = 0.7 × 400
= 280 J
The ratio of energy absorbed by the planet's surface to the energy reflected by the planet's surface is 5:2.
So the radiation that passes through the atmosphere transfers $\frac{5}{7}$ of its energy to the surface.
Energy absorbed by the surface = $\frac{5}{7} \times 280$
= **200 J**

[2 marks for the correct answer, otherwise 1 mark for correctly calculating the energy of the radiation that is transmitted through the atmosphere]

b) The temperature of the surface of the planet will decrease *[1 mark]* because the moon will block radiation from the star from reaching the planet and transferring energy to the surface *[1 mark]*.

Page 25 — Energy Resources

1 a) To find the total percentage greater than 10 m/s, multiply the height of each bar to the right of 10 m/s by its width, then add them all together:
Percentage time = (7 × 2) + (5 × 4) + (2 × 4) + (1 × 4)
= **46%**

[2 marks for correct answer, otherwise 1 mark for correctly reading widths and heights of the correct bars from the graph]

b) The hydroelectric system is most likely to allow the residents of the village to meet their energy needs *[1 mark]*, as it will provide the most constant supply of electricity *[1 mark]*. The supply from wind turbines is less reliable as power cannot be generated if there is not enough / too much wind *[1 mark]*, and so the turbines may not be able generate as much power as is needed at a given time on a given day *[1 mark]*. The power output from solar panels also varies depending on how sunny it is *[1 mark]*, but will always be at a maximum around the middle of the day, and not in the evening when the village needs the most electricity *[1 mark]*.

Section 5 — Solids, Liquids and Gases

Page 26: Density

1 a) Rearrange $\rho = m \div V$ for V:

$V = m \div \rho$

Calculate the total volume of the block of aerogel:

$V = 0.50 \div 1.50$

$\quad = 0.333...\ m^3$

Divide the volume below the waterline by the total volume and multiply by 100 to get the percentage of the volume beneath the waterline:

percentage of volume $= \dfrac{5 \times 10^{-4}}{0.333...} \times 100$

$\quad = \mathbf{0.15\%}$

[4 marks for correct answer, otherwise 1 mark for correctly rearranging $\rho = m \div V$ for V, 1 mark for correct substitution into $V = m \div \rho$ and 1 mark for correctly calculating the total volume of the aerogel]

b) $\rho = m \div V$

Rearranging for m gives:

$m = \rho \times V$

mass produced in 24 hours $= \rho \times V$

$\quad\quad\quad = 1.50 \times 0.360$

$\quad\quad\quad = 0.54\ kg$

minutes in one day $= 24 \times 60 = 1440$ minutes

rate of production $=$ mass $\div$ time

$\quad\quad\quad = 0.54 \div 1440$

$\quad\quad\quad = 0.000375\ kg/min$

Convert kg/min to g/min:

$0.000375 \times 1000 = \mathbf{0.375\ g/min}$

[5 marks for the correct answer, otherwise 1 mark for correctly rearranging $\rho = m \div V$ for m, 1 mark for correct substitution into $m = \rho \times V$, 1 mark for correctly calculating the mass of aerogel produced in 24 hours and 1 mark for dividing this mass by the number of minutes in a day]

Page 27-28: Specific Heat Capacity and Changes of State

1 a) The change in temperature of the water is:

$\Delta T = 30 - 27$

$\quad = 3\ °C$

The energy transferred from the ball to the water is:

$\Delta Q = m \times c \times \Delta T$

$\quad = 1.0 \times 4200 \times 3$

$\quad = 12\ 600\ J$

Rearrange the equation for $\Delta \theta$:

$\Delta T = \dfrac{\Delta Q}{m \times c}$

50 g = 0.05 kg

The ball loses 12 600 J, so the change in temperature of the ball is:

$\Delta T = \dfrac{\Delta Q}{m \times c}$

$\quad = \dfrac{12\ 600}{0.05 \times 900}$

$\quad = 280\ °C$

The water and ball end up at the same temperature of 30 °C, so the initial temperature of the ball is:

$30 + 280 = \mathbf{310\ °C}$

[5 marks for the correct answer, otherwise 1 mark for the correct substitution into $\Delta Q = m \times c \times \Delta T$, 1 mark for calculating the energy transferred from the ball to the water, 1 mark for correct substitution into $\Delta T = \dfrac{\Delta Q}{m \times c}$ and 1 mark for correct calculation of the change in temperature of the ball]

b)

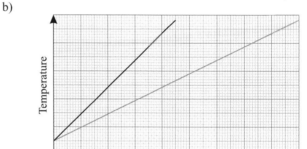

[1 mark for correctly drawn line]

The energy needed to change the temperature of a substance by a given amount is proportional to its mass. Since ball B has half the mass of ball A, half the energy is needed to change the temperature and of ball B by a given amount (compared to ball A) *[1 mark]*. Energy is transferred to ball B at the same constant rate as ball A, so the amount of energy needed for a given temperature change will be supplied in half the time *[1 mark]*.

2 a) $\Delta Q = m \times c \times \Delta T$

Rearranging for m gives:

$m = \dfrac{\Delta Q}{c \times \Delta T}$

$\quad = \dfrac{740}{217 \times 30}$

$\quad = 0.113...$

$\quad = \mathbf{0.11\ kg\ (to\ 2\ s.f.)}$

[4 marks for the correct answer, otherwise 1 mark for correct rearrangement, 1 mark for correct substitution and 1 mark for the correct unrounded answer]

b) The tin is changing state *[1 mark]*. Energy is being used to break the intermolecular bonds rather than raise the temperature / energy is transferred to the potential energy stores of the particles rather than their kinetic energy stores
[1 mark].

c) 30 g = 0.03 kg
The change in temperature of the liquid ammonia is:
$\Delta T_l = -33 - (-60)$
$= 27\,°C$
The energy needed to raise the temperature of the liquid ammonia is:
$\Delta Q = m \times c_l \times \Delta T_l$
$= 0.03 \times 4700 \times 27$
$= 3807\,J$
The change in temperature of the gaseous ammonia is:
$\Delta T_g = -10 - (-33)$
$= 23\,°C$
The energy needed to raise the temperature of the gaseous ammonia is:
$\Delta Q = m \times c_g \times \Delta T_g$
$= 0.03 \times 2060 \times 23$
$= 1421.4\,J$
The total energy supplied is equal to the sum of the energy used to raise the temperature of the liquid ammonia, the energy used to boil the ammonia, and the energy needed to raise the temperature of the gaseous ammonia:
46.3 kJ = 46 300 J
So the energy used to boil the ammonia
= 46 300 − 3807 − 1421.4
= 41 071.6
= 41 100 J (to 3 s.f.)
[5 marks for correct answer, otherwise 1 mark for correct substitution into $\Delta Q = m \times c_l \times \Delta T_l$ or $\Delta Q = m \times c_g \times \Delta T_g$, 1 mark for correctly calculating the energy needed to raise the temperature of the liquid ammonia, 1 mark for correctly calculating the energy needed to raise the temperature of the gaseous ammonia and 1 mark for calculating the correct unrounded answer]

Pages 29-30: Particle Motion in Gases

1 a) The pressure outside an underwater air bubble decreases as it rises, so the pressure inside the bubble is greater than the pressure outside the bubble *[1 mark]*. The volume inside the bubble increases until the pressure inside the bubble is equal to the pressure outside / the force acting outwards on the bubble is greater than the forces acting inwards on the bubble, so the volume of the bubble increases *[1 mark]*.

b) Read off values for the pressure from the graph:
Pressure at depth of 10 m = p_1 = 2 kPa
Pressure at depth of 25 m = p_2 = 3.5 kPa
Rearrange $p_1 V_1 = p_2 V_2$ for V_2:
$V_2 = p_1 V_1 \div p_2$
$= (2 \times 1000) \div 3.5$
$= 571.42...$
= 570 cm^3 (to 2 s.f.)
[4 marks for the correct answer, otherwise 1 mark for reading the correct values from the graph, 1 mark for correct use of pV = constant and 1 mark for correct unrounded answer]

The units for pressure and volume don't need to be converted here since the equation is a ratio.

2 a) The outward force acting on the walls of the cylinder is equal to the sum of the forces exerted by all the particles in the cylinder on the cylinder walls *[1 mark]*.
The outward gas pressure is equal to the net force acting per unit area on the cylinder walls *[1 mark]*.
If there are fewer oxygen particles in the cylinder, then collisions between the particles and the walls will occur less often, so the net force and pressure will also decrease *[1 mark]*.

b) As the oxygen cylinder is carried up the mountain, its temperature decreases. The average amount of energy in the kinetic energy stores of the oxygen particles is proportional to their temperature, so this also decreases *[1 mark]*.
The energy in the kinetic energy store of an oxygen particle is proportional to its speed squared. So the average speed of the oxygen particles also decreases *[1 mark]*.
As the particles are travelling more slowly, they hit the walls with less force and less often, meaning that the outward force acting on the cylinder decreases *[1 mark]*. The area of the cylinder remains the same but the net force decreases as the cylinder is carried up the mountain, so the pressure must also decrease *[1 mark]*.

Pages 31-32: Pressure

1 a) Difference in pressure = pressure due to oil + pressure due to water
So, pressure due to oil = difference in pressure − pressure due to water
First calculate the pressure due to water:
Pressure due to column of liquid, $p = h \times \rho \times g$
Oil is 2 cm thick, so 5 cm below surface of the oil is 3 cm below surface of the water. 3 cm = 0.03 m.
Pressure due to water = 0.03 × 1000 × 10
= 300 Pa
Difference in pressure = 470.4 Pa
So, pressure due to oil = 470.4 − 300
= 170.4 Pa
Rearrange pressure equation for density:
$\rho = \dfrac{p}{h \times g}$
Thickness of oil = 2 cm = 0.02 m

So the density of the oil is:
$\rho = \dfrac{170.4}{0.02 \times 10} = 852 = $ **900 kg/m^3 (to 1 s.f.)**
[5 marks for correct answer, otherwise 1 mark for correct substitution into pressure equation to find pressure due to water, 1 mark for correct calculation of pressure due to water, 1 mark for correct rearrangement of pressure equation for density and 1 mark for correct substitution to find density of oil]

b)

[1 mark]

Oil is less dense than water *[1 mark]*.

Pressure is directly proportional to density, so the pressure increases with depth at a greater rate in water compared to oil *[1 mark]*.

2 a) Pressure inside the can = 510 kPa = 510 000 Pa

Height of aerosol can = 20 cm = 0.2 m

Radius of aerosol can = 2.5 cm = 0.025 m

Surface area of aerosol can = $(2 \times \pi \times 0.025) \times (0.025 + 0.2)$
$$= 0.03534... \text{ m}^3$$

$p = \dfrac{F}{A}$ so $F = p \times A$
$$= 510\,000 \times 0.03534...$$
$$= 18\,024.88... \text{ N}$$
$$= \mathbf{18\,000 \text{ N (to 3 s.f.)}}$$

[5 marks for correct answer, otherwise 1 mark for correct calculation of surface area, 1 mark for correct rearrangement of pressure equation, 1 mark for correct substitution into pressure equation and 1 mark for correct unrounded answer]

b) Pressure inside the can = 510 kPa = 510 000 Pa

Pressure in water = $510\,000 = h \times \rho \times g$

$h = \dfrac{p}{\rho \times g}$

$h = \dfrac{510\,000}{1000 \times 10}$
$$= 51$$
$$= \mathbf{50 \text{ m (to 1 s.f.)}}$$

[3 marks for correct answer, otherwise 1 mark for rearranging the equation, 1 mark for correct substitution]

c) 1.1 kJ = 1100 J

200 g = 0.2 kg

Find the temperature rise that results from the increased energy:

$\Delta Q = m \times c \times \Delta T$

$\Delta T = \dfrac{\Delta Q}{m \times c}$
$$= \dfrac{1100}{0.2 \times 620}$$
$$= 8.87... \text{ K}$$

The gas's new temperature = 293 + 8.87... = 301.87... K

Calculate the gas's new pressure:

$\dfrac{p_1}{T_1} = \dfrac{p_2}{T_2}$

$p_2 = \dfrac{p_1 \times T_2}{T_1}$
$$= \dfrac{510\,000 \times 301.87...}{293}$$
$$= 525\,440.9... \text{ Pa}$$
$$= \mathbf{530\,000 \text{ Pa (to 2 s.f.)}}$$

[4 marks for correct answer, otherwise 1 mark for correctly calculating the increase in the gas's temperature, 1 mark for correctly calculating the gas's new temperature and 1 mark for calculating the correct unrounded answer]

Section 6 — Magnetism and Electromagnetism

Pages 33-34: Electromagnetism

1 a) i) Current from the circuit flows round the coil, which produces a magnetic field around the coil.
This magnetic field interacts with the magnetic field of the magnets, so the parts of the coil perpendicular to the field, i.e. the sides of the coil, feel a force due to the motor effect *[1 mark]*.
The forces on the two sides act in opposite directions which causes the coil (and so the pointer) to rotate and the spring to stretch (or compress). As the spring stretches (or compresses) it applies a force to the coil in the opposite direction to the force from the motor effect *[1 mark]*.
The force applied by the spring increases as the coil rotates more. The forces will eventually balance and the pointer will come to a rest *[1 mark]*.
The larger the current through the coil, the larger the force due to the motor effect, and the more the pointer will turn before the forces balance *[1 mark]*.
When the current stops flowing, the force disappears and the spring returns the pointer back to its original position *[1 mark]*. If the current is reversed then the pointer moves in the opposite direction because the force on each side of the coil is reversed (Fleming's left-hand rule) *[1 mark]*.

ii) The magnetic field produced by the curved magnets is always perpendicular to the current through the coil as it rotates, so the force on the coil is constant *[1 mark]*.
This allows the scale to be linear *[1 mark]*.

iii) E.g.

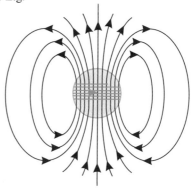

[1 mark for correct shaped field lines that are parallel and equally spaced inside the coil and curved outside, 1 mark for the correct direction marked on the magnetic field lines]

b) i) E.g. pass known currents through the galvanometer and mark them on the scale where the pointer comes to a rest *[1 mark]*.

ii) Any two from: e.g. decrease the strength of the magnets/ magnetic field *[1 mark]*. / Decrease the number of turns on the coil *[1 mark]*. / Use a stiffer spring *[1 mark]*.

The overall force needs to be smaller or the spring stiffer so that the pointer doesn't move as far for the same current. To decrease the force, the strength of the magnetic field or the number of wires needs to be decreased.

Pages 35-36: Transformers and Loudspeakers

1 a) i) $1.2\ kA = 1.2 \times 1000 = 1200\ A$

Using $\dfrac{\text{input voltage}}{\text{output voltage}} = \dfrac{\text{primary turns}}{\text{secondary turns}}$ and $V_p I_p = V_s I_s$

$I_s = \dfrac{I_p V_p}{V_s} = I_p \times \dfrac{\text{primary turns}}{\text{secondary turns}}$

$= 1200 \times \dfrac{60\,000}{45\,000}$

$= \mathbf{1600\ A}\ (= \mathbf{1.6 \times 10^3\ A})$

[3 marks for correct answer, otherwise 1 mark for getting an expression involving current and number of turns and 1 mark for correct substitution]

ii) Any one from: e.g. Assume 100% efficiency / no energy losses / no energy transferred to the thermal energy stores of the surroundings *[1 mark]*.

b)   D *[1 mark]*

$\dfrac{\text{input voltage}}{\text{output voltage}} = \dfrac{\text{primary turns}}{\text{secondary turns}}$,

so output voltage = input voltage $\times \dfrac{\text{secondary turns}}{\text{primary turns}}$

The input voltage stays the same, so to double the output voltage the ratio $\dfrac{\text{secondary turns}}{\text{primary turns}}$ must double. This happens if either the number of turns on the secondary coil is doubled or the number of turns on the primary coil is halved.

c)   Iron becomes magnetic in the presence of a magnetic field *[1 mark]*. However, it is magnetically soft *[1 mark]*, so it loses induced magnetism quickly when the external magnetic field is removed *[1 mark]*.
This is useful in a transformer as the core needs to magnetise and demagnetise many times a second *[1 mark]*.

2 a)   It will be larger *[1 mark]*

The faster the movement, the greater the rate of change of magnetic flux through the coil. This means a larger voltage is induced across the coil, and so a larger induced current flows.

b) i) The coil of wire should be put into a magnetic field that is perpendicular to the wire at all times/a radial magnetic field/a magnetic field caused by one pole inside the coil and one pole around it *[1 mark]*.
Sound waves hitting the cone cause it to vibrate *[1 mark]*. This causes the coil of wire to vibrate back and forth inside the magnetic field *[1 mark]* which induces a current in the coil of wire due to the generator effect *[1 mark]*.

ii) The strength of the electrical signal can be increased by putting the coil into a stronger magnetic field *[1 mark]*, and by increasing the number of turns on the coil *[1 mark]*.

The speed of the coil's motion in the magnetic field is determined by the sound wave, so can't be increased to strengthen the signal.

Section 7 — Radioactivity and Particles

Pages 37-39 — The Atomic Model and Nuclear Radiation

1 a) i) Beta decay *[1 mark]*

ii) E.g. $^{93}_{39}Y \rightarrow\ ^{93}_{40}Zr +\ ^{0}_{-1}e$
[2 marks for the correct answer, otherwise 1 mark for the correct symbol for a beta particle/electron or 1 mark for all the atomic and mass numbers correct]
You can use an e or β as the symbol for a beta-minus particle.

b) i) E.g. The mass number has decreased by 4, so the nucleus has lost 4 nucleons. This means the particle emitted was an alpha particle *[1 mark]*. The nucleus has lost 2 protons and 2 neutrons *[1 mark]*.

ii) $55 - 2 = 53$ *[1 mark]*

When a caesium nucleus emits an alpha particle to become iodine, it loses two protons, so its atomic number decreases by 2.

c)   A *[1 mark]*

In fusion, lighter elements fuse together to form heavier elements. Calcium is the only element with a lower atomic number than titanium in the list, so it's the only lighter element than titanium.

d)   There are different isotopes of some elements. Isotopes have the same atomic number but different mass numbers so an element doesn't have one fixed mass number *[1 mark]*.

2 a) i) 35 counts per minute *[1 mark, accept any answer between 32 cpm and 37 cpm]*

ii)

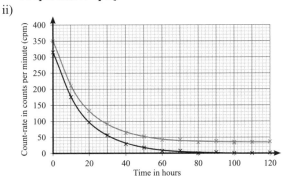

[2 marks for all points and line correctly plotted, otherwise 1 mark for all points being 35 cpm below the original curve]

Even if you got the answer to 2 a) i) wrong, you get full marks for 2 a) ii) if you drew the correct curve using your answer for 2 a) i).

b)   12 hours

Use the curve you drew in 2 a) ii) and work out the time taken for the count-rate to halve, e.g. from 315 cpm to 157.5 cpm.

[2 marks for correct answer found from the graph with background radiation removed, otherwise 1 mark for calculating an incorrect value for half life using the correct method but the original uncorrected graph]

c) i) Since the measurements are accurate to ± 5 cpm, the count rate will definitely be below 25 if the corrected count rate is below 20 cpm *[1 mark]*.
The water is safe to drink after 49 hours
[1 mark — accept any value between 48-50].

ii) Radioactivity is a random process. A single reading below 25 cpm does not necessarily indicate that the count-rate will stay below 25 cpm *[1 mark]*.

3 a) Gamma radiation *[1 mark]*

b) The gamma radiation should be directed through the blade towards the detector *[1 mark]*. The blade will reduce the amount of radiation reaching the detector *[1 mark]*. When there is a crack, less radiation will be absorbed and the count rate detected will increase, so the crack can be detected *[1 mark]*.

4 a) i) $^{131}_{53}\text{I} \rightarrow ^{131}_{54}\text{Xe} + ^{0}_{-1}\text{e}$ *[1 mark]*
$^{131}_{54}\text{Xe} \rightarrow ^{131}_{54}\text{Xe} + ^{0}_{0}\gamma$ *[1 mark]*

ii) Any two from: e.g. Iodine-131 decays to release gamma radiation which is penetrative enough to be detected outside of the body *[1 mark]*. / Iodine-131 doesn't give out alpha radiation, which would be very dangerous inside the body *[1 mark]*. / Iodine-131 doesn't have a really short half-life, which means that the sample will still emit radiation once it is in the patient, so it can be traced/a diagnosis can be made *[1 mark]*.

b) The gamma (or beta) radiation given out by the iodine-131 could pass out of the patient's body and irradiate others nearby *[1 mark]*.
Radiation can damage cells and so could cause damage to the people nearby *[1 mark]*.

Pages 40-41 — Fission and Fusion

1 a) E.g.
Contamination:
The risk posed by contamination, where the uranium-235 gets onto the workers' skin or if they breathe it in, is high as uranium-235 emits alpha particles which do a lot of damage inside the body.
The protective gloves and sealed zips of the suit shown protect against contamination as they stop radioactive particles getting on the worker's hands or into the suit. / The breathing mask protects against contamination as it stops the worker breathing in any radioactive particles in the air.
Irradiation:
The risk posed by irradiation if the workers are exposed to radiation is also high because uranium-235 emits gamma radiation which can easily penetrate deep into the body from outside and damage organs/tissues.
The radiation shielding material of the protective suit helps to protect against irradiation as some radiation will be blocked/absorbed before it reaches the body. / The sealed zips ensure that there are no gaps in the suit through which radiation could reach the body.
[1 mark for each correct description of a risk of irradiation and contamination, 1 mark for explaining how the suit protects against the irradiation risk described, 1 mark for explaining how the suit protects against the contamination risk described]

b) C *[1 mark]*
The first option cannot be correct as fission is a chain reaction, so more neutrons need to be released along with the products. The second and fourth options cannot be correct as the nucleus has to absorb a neutron to undergo fission.

2 a) C *[1 mark]*
Energy is released when an atom undergoes fission, so increasing the number of fissions increases the energy released.

b) Iodine-131 is dangerous when inhaled or ingested as beta radiation is ionising and can cause damage to the body internally *[1 mark]*.
If this iodine were absorbed by the thyroid, it would remain in the body for a long time / travel around the body in molecules made by the thyroid *[1 mark]*.
Ingesting a potassium iodide tablet with a stable iodine isotope allows the thyroid to absorb enough iodine in the form of a stable isotope, preventing the radioactive iodine-131 from being absorbed by the thyroid *[1 mark]*.
The stable iodine does no harm and the iodine-131 is then removed from the body, which minimises the time that the ionising radiation spends in the body and so minimises damage through irradiation *[1 mark]*.

Section 8 — Astrophysics

Pages 42-45 — Astrophysics

1 a) i) The universe is expanding, and so galaxy X is moving away from the Earth *[1 mark]*.
Red-shift occurs when an object that is emitting light is moving away from the observer, and so the wavelengths of the light from galaxy X are stretched out and the light is red-shifted *[1 mark]*.

ii) Read wavelengths of equivalent dark lines from the spectra and find difference between them:
E.g. reading fourth dark line:
Wavelength in spectrum B, $\lambda = 656$ nm
Wavelength in spectrum A = 670 nm
So, $\Delta\lambda = 670 - 656$
$= 14$ nm
$z = \dfrac{\Delta\lambda}{\lambda}$
$= \dfrac{14}{656}$
$= 0.021341...$
$= \mathbf{0.021}$ **(to 2 s.f.)**

(Accept between 0.019 and 0.023)
[4 marks for correct answer, otherwise 1 mark for reading correct pair of values from the spectra, 1 mark for correct substitution and 1 mark for correct unrounded answer]

b) Galaxy Y is further from Earth, and so the light emitted from it will undergo a larger red-shift *[1 mark]*.
The range of wavelengths in which the absorption lines sit has been shifted so much that these lines are no longer in the visible part of the spectrum *[1 mark]*.
The astronomer could observe the infrared radiation reaching Earth from galaxy Y (as the absorption lines will have been shifted into the infrared part of the electromagnetic spectrum) *[1 mark]*.

2 a) i) E.g.

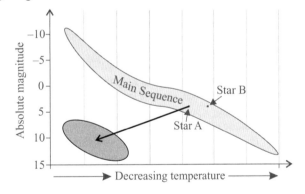

[1 mark for arrow drawn from star A to any point within the shaded region shown]

ii) The absolute magnitude is a measure of how bright a star would appear if it was a fixed distance from Earth, rather than of how bright that star actually appears *[1 mark]*.
So star B must be closer to Earth than star A, making it appear brighter *[1 mark]*.

b) i) orbital speed $= \dfrac{2\pi \times \text{orbital radius}}{\text{time period}}$, or $v = \dfrac{2 \times \pi \times r}{T}$
so $r = \dfrac{v \times T}{2 \times \pi}$
$v = 36$ km/s $= 36\ 000$ m/s
$T = 250$ days $= 6000$ hours
$= 360\ 000$ minutes $= 21\ 600\ 000$ s
$r = \dfrac{36\ 000 \times 21\ 600\ 000}{2 \times \pi}$
$= 1.2375... \times 10^{11}$
$= \mathbf{1.2 \times 10^{11}}$ **m (to 2 s.f.)**
[3 marks for correct answer, otherwise 1 mark for correct rearrangement of orbital speed equation and 1 mark for correct substitution into equation]

ii) speed $= \dfrac{\text{distance}}{\text{time}}$,
so time $= \dfrac{\text{distance}}{\text{speed}}$
time = time period of moon's orbit
distance = circumference $= 3.52 \times 10^{9}$ m
time $= \dfrac{3.52 \times 10^{9}}{815}$
$= 4\ 319\ 018.405...$
time for planet C to complete its orbit = 250 days
$= 21\ 600\ 000$ s
So the number of orbits completed by planet C's moon
$= 21\ 600\ 000 \div 4\ 319\ 018.405...$
$= 5.001...$
$= \mathbf{5}$ **(to nearest whole number)**
[4 marks for correct answer, otherwise 1 mark for correct rearrangement of speed equation, 1 mark for correct substitution into the equation and 1 mark for correct calculation of the orbital period of the moon]

3 a) i) Galaxy Q. $\dfrac{\Delta\lambda}{\lambda_0} = \dfrac{v}{c}$, so velocity is proportional to $\Delta\lambda$.
Galaxy Q has the larger change in wavelength, so it must have the greater velocity relative to Earth
[1 mark for the correct answer with justification].

ii) $\dfrac{\text{change in wavelength}}{\text{reference wavelength}} = \dfrac{\text{velocity of a galaxy}}{\text{speed of light}}$,
or $\dfrac{\lambda - \lambda_0}{\lambda_0} = \dfrac{v}{c}$
so $v = c \times \dfrac{\lambda - \lambda_0}{\lambda_0}$
From the spectrum of galaxy Q, $\lambda = 554$ nm
$v = (3.0 \times 10^{8}) \times \dfrac{554 - 486}{486}$
$= 41\ 975\ 308.641...$
$= \mathbf{42\ 000\ 000}$ **m/s (to 3 s.f.)**
(or 4.20×10^{7} m/s (to 3 s.f.))
[4 marks for correct answer, otherwise 1 mark for correct rearrangement of equation, 1 mark for correct reading of λ from the spectrum and 1 mark for correct substitution into equation]

b) Cosmic Microwave Background (CMB) radiation is low frequency microwave radiation which can be detected coming from all directions and all parts of the universe *[1 mark]*.
CMB radiation is believed to be radiation emitted soon after the 'Big Bang' *[1 mark]*, which has dropped in frequency as the universe has expanded and cooled *[1 mark]*.

c) The absorption spectrum of visible light observed from this galaxy would be shifted towards the blue end of the spectrum compared to an absorption spectrum caused by the same elements on Earth *[1 mark]*.
This is because the galaxy is moving towards Earth, and so the light observed from it will appear to have a shorter wavelength than when it was emitted *[1 mark]*.

Mixed Questions for Paper 1

Pages 46-50 — Mixed Questions for Paper 1

1 a) Thinking distance = speed of car × reaction time of the driver *[1 mark]*.
A person's reaction time is a constant, and so thinking distance is directly proportional to speed, making the graph of thinking distance against speed a straight line *[1 mark]*. When a car brakes, the brakes do work to transfer energy away from the kinetic energy store of the car, and so to stop the car, the brakes must do work equal to the total energy in the kinetic energy store of the car *[1 mark]*.
Work done = force × distance, and the braking force is assumed to be constant at the maximum force the brakes can apply, so the braking distance is proportional to the work done by the brakes *[1 mark]*.
The energy in the car's kinetic energy store = ½ × mass × (speed)^2, so braking distance is proportional to the speed of the car squared, which produces the curved graph of braking distance against speed *[1 mark]*.

b) Convert 33 m/s to mph:
Speed in mph = 33 ÷ 0.447 = 73.8... mph ≈ 74 mph
Evaluate both graphs at 74 mph:
Thinking distance = 22 m
Braking distance = 84 m
Stopping distance = 22 + 84
= **106 m**
[3 marks for correct answer, otherwise 1 mark for correctly converting the speed to mph and 1 mark for correctly reading distance from one of the graphs]

c) Thinking distance/reaction time is not affected by road conditions and so the thinking distance graph will remain the same *[1 mark]*. A slippery road means there will be less friction between the tyres and the road once the brakes have been applied *[1 mark]*. This will result in the car travelling further for the same speed *[1 mark]*, so the gradient of the braking distance graph will be greater at all speeds *[1 mark]*.

2 a) When the button is pressed, the switch closes and the circuit is complete, so the a.c. power supply provides a current through the coil of wire, which causes a magnetic field to be created around the coil *[1 mark]*.
The steel brake plate is inside the coil's magnetic field, so it becomes an induced magnet *[1 mark]*.
The brake plate is attracted to the steel rail and moves downwards so that it is in contact with the rail *[1 mark]*.
Friction between the brake plate and the rail acts in the opposite direction to the train's velocity and this resultant force causes the train to decelerate until it comes to a stop *[1 mark]*.

b) 0.4 MN = 0.4 × 10^6 = 400 000 N
$F = ma$
Rearrange for a to find the deceleration of the train:
$a = F ÷ m$
= 400 000 ÷ 200 000
= 2 m/s^2
Deceleration is negative acceleration, so:
$a = -2$ m/s^2
$v^2 = u^2 + (2 × a × s)$
Rearrange for s:
$s = \dfrac{v^2 - u^2}{2 × a}$
$= \dfrac{0^2 - 28^2}{2 × (-2)}$
= **196 m**

[5 marks for correct answer, otherwise 1 mark for correct substitution into a = F ÷ m, 1 mark for correctly calculating the deceleration, 1 mark for rearranging v^2 = u^2 + (2 × a × s) for s and 1 mark for correct substitution into s = $\dfrac{v^2 - u^2}{2 × a}$]

Alternatively you could calculate the energy in the train's kinetic energy store using KE = ½ × m × v^2. Then rearrange the work done equation, W = F × d, to find the distance travelled.

3 a) i) The stone is travelling downwards *[1 mark]* with a constant acceleration *[1 mark]*.
ii) The maximum height is reached when the stone's velocity reaches 0 m/s for the first time, which is 0.11 s after it hits the water. The distance travelled during this time is equal to the area under the graph up to this time.
Area of a triangle is 0.5 × base × height,
so maximum height of the stone = 0.5 × 0.11 × 1.0
= **0.055 m**
[2 marks for the correct answer, otherwise 1 mark for reading the correct values from the graph]

b)

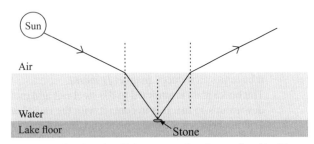

Sun

Air

Water

Lake floor   Stone

[1 mark for drawing light rays so that the angle of incidence on the stone is equal to the angle of reflection and 1 mark for drawing the light refracting away from the normal as it leaves the water]

4 a) The useful energy transferred by the lift is the energy transferred to the gravitational potential energy stores of the lift and its contents.

Total mass of lift plus contents
$m = 1200 + 700$
$\quad = 1900$ kg
$GPE = m \times g \times h$
$\quad\quad = 1900 \times 10 \times 300$
$\quad\quad = 5\,700\,000$ J
Efficiency = useful energy output ÷
$\quad\quad\quad$ total energy output × 100%
9500 kJ = 9 500 000 J
So efficiency = 5 700 000 ÷ 9 500 000 × 100%
$\quad\quad\quad\quad = \mathbf{60\%}$

[4 marks for the correct answer, otherwise 1 mark for correct substitution into $GPE = m \times g \times h$, 1 mark for calculating the energy transferred to the gravitational potential energy stores of the lift and its contents and 1 mark for correct substitution into the efficiency equation]

b) $P = I \times V$, so
$I = \dfrac{P}{V}$
$\quad = \dfrac{75}{120}$
$\quad = 0.625$ A

$V = I \times R$, so
$R = \dfrac{V}{I}$
$\quad \dfrac{120}{0.625}$
$\quad = \mathbf{192\ \Omega}$

[5 marks for the correct answer, otherwise 1 mark for substituting into $P = I \times V$, 1 mark for correct value of I, 1 mark for rearranging $V = I \times R$ and 1 mark for substituting into rearranged equation]

c) Assuming that the coin has no initial velocity, so no energy in its kinetic energy store before it starts falling, and that there is no energy lost due to friction/air resistance to the surroundings:

Energy in the coin's gravitational potential energy store at the top = energy in the coin's kinetic energy store at the bottom
$m \times g \times h = \dfrac{1}{2} \times m \times v^2$
Cancel m from both sides:
$g \times h = \dfrac{1}{2} \times v^2$
$v = \sqrt{2 \times g \times h} = \sqrt{2 \times 10 \times 300} = 77.45...$
$\quad\quad\quad\quad\quad\quad\quad\quad = \mathbf{77\ m/s\ (to\ 2\ s.f.)}$

[5 marks for the correct answer, otherwise 1 mark for equating the energy in the gravitational potential energy store of the coin at the top with the energy in the kinetic energy store of the coin at the bottom, 1 mark for stating the correct assumptions, 1 mark for correct rearrangement of the equation and 1 mark for correct substitution]

You could also use $v^2 = u^2 + (2 \times a \times s)$ to calculate the final speed of the coin.

5 a) Use $\rho = m \div V$ to calculate the density of the neutron star:
$\rho = (2.1 \times 10^{30}) \div (1.4 \times 10^{13})$
$\quad = 1.5 \times 10^{17}$ kg/m³
Rearrange $\rho = m \div V$ for m:
$m = \rho \times V$
$\quad = 1.5 \times 10^{17} \times 1.0 \times 10^{-6}$
$\quad = \mathbf{1.5 \times 10^{11}\ kg}$

[5 marks for the correct answer, otherwise 1 mark for correct substitution into $\rho = m \div V$, 1 mark for the correct value of ρ for a neutron star, 1 mark for rearranging the equation for m and 1 mark for correct substitution into $m = \rho \times V$]

b) E.g. Solid matter on Earth is made of atoms closely packed together, which are mostly empty space *[1 mark]*. Neutrons do not contain this empty space and so have more mass per unit volume *[1 mark]*.

c) The number of seconds in one year is:
$60 \times 60 \times 24 \times 365 = 3.1536 \times 10^7$ s
Calculate the energy released by the Sun in one year:
$(4 \times 10^{26}) \times 3.1536 \times 10^7 = 1.26144 \times 10^{34}$ J
So the number of years it would take the Sun to release 1×10^{44} J is:
$(1 \times 10^{44}) \div (1.26144 \times 10^{34}) = 7.92... \times 10^9$
$\quad\quad\quad\quad\quad\quad\quad\quad = \mathbf{8 \times 10^9\ years\ (to\ 1\ s.f.)}$

[3 marks for the correct answer, otherwise 1 mark for dividing 1×10^{44} by the amount of energy released by the Sun in either a year or a second and 1 mark for correctly converting to years from seconds at some point in the calculation]

d) The energy from the nearby star is transferred to the kinetic energy stores of the particles of the gas cloud *[1 mark]*, which causes the particles to move faster and so to collide more often / to collide with more force *[1 mark]*. This results in an increase in pressure in the gas cloud *[1 mark]*.

e) i) nuclear fusion *[1 mark]*
   ii) E.g. the temperature and pressure in the gas cloud are too low *[1 mark]*. The low temperature means that positively charged nuclei within the cloud are not moving fast enough to overcome the forces of electrostatic repulsion between them *[1 mark]*. This combined with the low pressure in the gas cloud means that nuclei cannot get close enough together to fuse *[1 mark]*.

Mixed Questions for Paper 2

Pages 51-56 — Mixed Questions for Paper 2

1 a) i) Before the collision, the momentum of the club is:
$p = m \times v$
$= 0.40 \times 20$
$= 8$ kg m/s
The ball isn't moving, so it has a momentum of 0 kg m/s.
So the total momentum before the collision is 8 kg m/s.
After the collision, the momentum of the club is:
$p = m \times v$
$= 0.40 \times 15$
$= 6$ kg m/s
The total momentum before the collision must be equal to the total momentum after the collision, so the ball must have a momentum of:
$8 - 6 = 2$ kg m/s
45 g = 0.045 kg
$p = m \times v$
Rearrange the equation for v to find the size of ball's velocity:
$v = p \div m$
$= 2 \div 0.045$
$= 44.4...$
$= \textbf{44 m/s (to 2 s.f.)}$
[5 marks for correct answer, otherwise 1 mark for correctly calculating the total momentum before the collision, 1 mark for correct rearrangement, 1 mark for correct substitution into $v = p \div m$ and 1 mark for correct unrounded answer]

ii) The final velocity of the ball is 0 m/s, so:
$a = \dfrac{(v - u)}{t}$
$= \dfrac{0 - 3}{5}$
$= -0.6$ m/s²
$F = m \times a$
$= 0.045 \times 0.6$
$= \textbf{0.027 N}$
[4 marks for correct answer, otherwise 1 mark for correct substitution into $a = \dfrac{(v-u)}{t}$, 1 mark for calculating the acceleration correctly and 1 mark for correct substitution into $F = m \times a$]

b) $F = \dfrac{(mv - mu)}{t}$, so the change in velocity of the ball is directly proportional to the contact time *[1 mark]*. Since the force and golf ball mass are the same, the velocity of the second ball after it is hit will be greater due to its increased contact time *[1 mark]*.

2 a) The planet's speed is constant, but its direction is constantly changing, so its velocity is changing *[1 mark]*. Since acceleration is the change in velocity over time, it is constantly accelerating *[1 mark]*.

b) i) E.g.

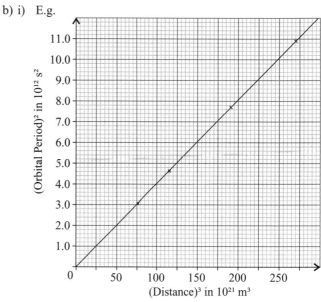

[1 mark for correctly plotting the point, 1 mark for suitable straight line of best fit]

ii) Comparing Kepler's Third Law, $T^2 = k \times r^3$, to the equation of a straight line, $y = mx + c$.
$y = T^2$, $m = k$, $x = r^3$ and $c = 0$
So Kepler's constant, k = gradient of the graph, m
E.g. $k = \dfrac{\text{change in } y}{\text{change in } x}$
$= \dfrac{10.1 \times 10^{12} - 0}{250 \times 10^{21} - 0}$
$= \textbf{4.04} \times \textbf{10}^{-11}$ **s²/m³**

(Accept between 4.00×10^{-11} s²/m³ and 4.08×10^{-11} s²/m³)
[2 marks for correct answer, otherwise 1 mark for attempt to calculate gradient]

c) The 160 GHz radiation is Cosmic Microwave Background (CMB) radiation *[1 mark]*.
It is believed to be leftover radiation from soon after the Big Bang explosion which caused the universe to begin expanding *[1 mark]*.
This background radiation has dropped in frequency as the universe has expanded and cooled *[1 mark]*.

3 a) Power of electricity supplied to the device = 1.843 GW
$$= 1.843 \times 10^9 \text{ W}$$
Power of electricity leaving device $= \frac{99}{100} \times 1.843 \times 10^9$
$$= 1.824... \times 10^9 \text{ W}$$
$P = I \times V$, so
$V = P \div I$
$I = 166 \text{ kA} = 166 \times 1000 = 166\,000 \text{ A}$
$V = 1.824... \times 10^9 \div 166\,000$
$$= 10\,991.385... \text{ V}$$
$$= \mathbf{11\,000 \text{ V} \text{ (to 3 s.f.)}}$$
[5 marks for correct answer, otherwise 1 mark for correct calculation of power of electricity leaving device, 1 mark for correct rearrangement for voltage, 1 mark for correct substitution for voltage and 1 mark for correct unrounded answer]

b) The pitch of the humming sound will get lower *[1 mark]* since the decrease in the a.c. frequency will also cause a decrease in the frequency of the sound *[1 mark]*.

c) Find energy transferred when the current flows:
$P = \frac{W}{t}$, so $W = P \times t$
$P = 0.31 \text{ GW} = 0.31 \times 10^9 = 3.1 \times 10^8 \text{ W}$
$W = 3.1 \times 10^8 \times 0.55$
$$= 1.705 \times 10^8 \text{ J}$$
$E = Q \times V$, so to find charge:
$Q = E \div V$
$V = 380 \text{ kV} = 3.8 \times 10^5 \text{ V}$
$Q = (1.705 \times 10^8) \div (3.8 \times 10^5)$
$$= 448.684... \text{ C}$$
$$= \mathbf{450 \text{ C} \text{ (to 2 s.f.)}}$$
[5 marks for correct answer, otherwise 1 mark for correct substitution to find energy transferred, 1 mark for correct calculation of energy transferred, 1 mark for correct rearrangement for charge and 1 mark for correct substitution for charge]
OR
Find current that flows through the cable into the car:
$P = I \times V$, so $I = P \div V$,
$P = 0.31 \text{ GW} = 0.31 \times 10^9 = 3.1 \times 10^8 \text{ W}$
$V = 380 \text{ kV} = 3.8 \times 10^5 \text{ V}$
so $I = 3.1 \times 10^8 \div 3.8 \times 10^5$
$$= 815.78... \text{ A}$$
Find charge that is transferred in 0.55 s:
$Q = I \times t$
$$= 815.78... \times 0.55$$
$$= 448.684... \text{ C}$$
$$= \mathbf{450 \text{ C} \text{ (to 2 s.f.)}}$$
[5 marks for correct answer, otherwise 1 mark for correct rearrangement for current, 1 mark for correct substitution to find current, 1 mark for correct calculation of current and 1 mark for correct substitution for charge]

d) E.g. the air rushing past the car as it travels at high speeds may cause it to gain or lose electrons, leading to the build-up of a static charge on the car *[1 mark]*.

4 a) Calculate the energy transferred to the water:
$m = 100 \text{ g} = 0.1 \text{ kg}$
$\Delta Q = m \times c \times \Delta T$
$$= 0.1 \times 4200 \times (61 - 25)$$
$$= 15\,120 \text{ J}$$
Assume 15 120 J was supplied by the heater.
$E = I \times V \times t$, so $I = \frac{E}{V \times t}$
$t = 5 \text{ minutes} = 300 \text{ s}$
$I = \frac{15\,120}{12 \times 300}$
$$= \mathbf{4.2 \text{ A}}$$
[5 marks for correct answer, otherwise 1 mark for correct substitution into change in thermal energy equation, 1 mark for correct calculation of energy transferred, 1 mark for correct rearrangement of $E = I \times V \times t$ for current, 1 mark for correct substitution to find the current]

b) As the temperature of the water decreases, the amount of energy in the particles' kinetic energy stores will also decrease *[1 mark]*, so they will move more slowly *[1 mark]*. The particles have less energy to overcome the forces of attraction between them, and so become closer together *[1 mark]*.

c) Draw a tangent at (1000, 30)
E.g.

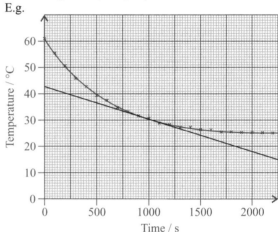

rate of temperature change = gradient of tangent
$$= \frac{18 - 40}{2000 - 225}$$
$$= -0.01239...$$
$$= \mathbf{-0.012 \text{ °C/s}}$$
(Accept any answer between –0.014 °C/s and –0.010 °C/s)
[3 marks for correct answer, otherwise 1 mark for correctly drawn tangent and 1 mark for attempt to calculate gradient]

d) i) E.g.

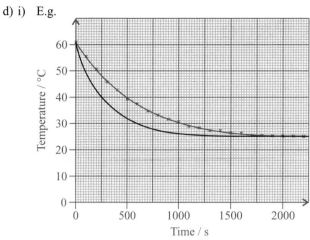

[1 mark for drawing oil curve with same start and end points as water curve, 1 mark for drawing oil curve with steeper initial gradient than water curve]

ii) Both substances cool to the same (room) temperature, so the curves must have the same start and end points *[1 mark]*. However, olive oil has a lower specific heat capacity than water, meaning that less energy must be transferred away from it to produce a given drop in temperature *[1 mark]*.

So the oil reaches its final temperature more quickly than the water and the initial gradient of its cooling curve is steeper *[1 mark]*.

5 a) $V_P \times I_P = V_S \times I_S$

So $V_S = \dfrac{V_P \times I_P}{I_S}$

40 mA = 0.04 A

1840 mA = 1.84 A

$V_s = \dfrac{230 \times 0.04}{1.84}$

= 5 V

$\dfrac{V_P}{V_S} = \dfrac{N_P}{N_S}$

So $N_s = N_P \times \dfrac{V_S}{V_P}$

$= 920 \times \dfrac{5}{230}$

= 20 turns

[5 marks for correct answer, otherwise 1 mark for correctly rearranging $V_P \times I_P = V_S \times I_S$, 1 mark for correct substitution, 1 mark for correctly calculating V_S, 1 mark for correct substitution into $\dfrac{V_P}{V_S} = \dfrac{N_P}{N_S}$]

As you're dealing with the ratio of the currents here, it actually only matters that both currents are given in the same unit — so you don't need to convert from mA to A to get the right answer.

b) E.g. for a voltage to be induced in the secondary coil, there must be a change in the magnetic field through it *[1 mark]*. The magnetic field through the secondary coil is produced by the current flowing through the primary coil *[1 mark]*.

An alternating voltage gives rise to an alternating current and so a changing magnetic field, whereas a direct voltage and so current would produce a constant (unchanging) magnetic field *[1 mark]*.

Equations Page

Here are some equations you might find useful — you'll be given these equations in the real exams.

(final speed)^2 = (initial speed)^2 + (2 × acceleration × distance moved) $$v^2 = u^2 + (2 \times a \times s)$$	
energy transferred = current × voltage × time	$E = I \times V \times t$
frequency = $\dfrac{1}{\text{time period}}$	$f = \dfrac{1}{T}$
power = $\dfrac{\text{work done}}{\text{time taken}}$	$P = \dfrac{W}{t}$
power = $\dfrac{\text{energy transferred}}{\text{time taken}}$	$P = \dfrac{W}{t}$
pressure × volume = constant	$p_1 \times V_1 = p_2 \times V_2$
$\dfrac{\text{pressure}}{\text{temperature}}$ = constant	$\dfrac{p_1}{T_1} = \dfrac{p_2}{T_2}$
orbital speed = $\dfrac{2\pi \times \text{orbital radius}}{\text{time period}}$	$v = \dfrac{2 \times \pi \times r}{T}$

Assume the acceleration due to gravity is g = 10 m/s^2.

PAPER 2

force = $\dfrac{\text{change in momentum}}{\text{time taken}}$

change in thermal energy = mass × specific heat capacity × change in temperature
$$\Delta Q = m \times c \times \Delta T$$

$\dfrac{\text{change of wavelength}}{\text{wavelength}} = \dfrac{\text{velocity of a galaxy}}{\text{speed of light}}$

$$\dfrac{\lambda - \lambda_0}{\lambda_0} = \dfrac{\Delta \lambda}{\lambda_0} = \dfrac{v}{c}$$

PE9QI41